THE BOOK OF INSECTS

Selections by Arabella Buckley & Julia McNair Wright

Teacher Guide

Brett Vaden & Laura Bateman

☾ MEMORIA PRESS

The Grasshopper

by the Greek of Anacreon

translated by Abraham Cowley

Happy insect, what can be
In happiness compared to thee?
Fed with nourishment divine,
The dewy morning's gentle wine!
Nature waits upon thee still,
And thy verdant cup does fill;
Thou dost drink, and dance, and sing,
Happier than the happiest king!
All the fields which thou dost see,
All the plants belong to thee;
All the summer hours produce,
Fertile made with early juice.
Man for thee does sow and plow,
Farmer he, and landlord thou!

Thou dost innocently enjoy;
Nor does thy luxury destroy.
The shepherd gladly heareth thee,
More harmonious than he.
Thee country folk with gladness hear,
Prophet of the ripened year!
To thee, of all things upon earth,
Life is no longer than thy mirth.
Happy insect! happy thou,
Dost neither age nor winter know;
But when thou'st drunk, and danced, and sung
Thy fill, the flowery leaves among,
Sated with thy summer feast,
Thou retir'st to endless rest.

MEMORIA PRESS

www.MemoriaPress.com

THE BOOK OF INSECTS
Selections by Arabella Buckley & Julia McNair Wright
TEACHER GUIDE
Brett Vaden & Laura Bateman
ISBN 978-1-61538-035-0

First Edition © 2011 Memoria Press | 0521

Cover illustration by Jan van Kessel, Sr.

Table of Contents

Goals

1. Retain major astronomy facts: fifteen brightest stars; constellations of summer triangle, Orion, and spring sky; planets' names, order from the sun, and special facts about each. See *The Book of Astronomy* Final Exam.

2. Be able to comprehend what an insect is, specifically: 1) that they are animals with a body made of rings and divided into three parts, and that they have six legs and either four or two wings, 2) that they are small in size but big in number, 3) know how they grow, 4) their general abilities and purpose in the world (i.e., benefits to man and nature), and 5) some of their negative effects on man.

3. Memorize the stages of complete and incomplete metamorphosis:

   Incomplete — egg, nymph, adult

   Complete — egg, larva, pupa, adult

   Memorize eight orders of insects, scientific and common names, kind of metamorphosis, two main traits/characteristics:

   Odonata (toothed) — Dragonflies and Damselflies; incomplete metamorphosis; water nymphs and needle-like abdomen

   Orthoptera (straight-winged) — Grasshoppers and Crickets; incomplete metamorphosis; fan-like hind wings and leathery front wings

   Dictyoptera (net-winged) — Cockroaches and Mantids; incomplete metamorphosis; fan-like hind wings and leathery front wings

   Hemiptera (half-winged) — True Bugs; incomplete metamorphosis; first half of wing is rough and tip is smooth

   Diptera (two-winged) — Flies; complete metamorphosis; soft body and sucking mouthparts

   Coleoptera (sheath-winged) — Beetles; complete metamorphosis; front wings are hard and meet down the middle of the back

   Lepidoptera (scale-winged) — Butterflies and Moths; complete metamorphosis; large wings and coiling mouthparts

   Hymenoptera (membrane-winged) — Bees, Wasps, and Ants; complete metamorphosis; slender waist and stingers

4. Be able to identify by sight the common names of several different insects, to what order each belongs, and where each may be found (e.g., pond, house).

Model Lesson Plan

Review

1. Astronomy: a) recite fifteen brightest stars and planets (with facts) in order from the sun; b) identify constellations on overhead or board

2. Insects: a) recite orders of insects, scientific and common names, kind of metamorphosis, two main traits/characteristics;

   b) recite stages of complete and incomplete metamorphosis;

   c) identify common names of insects (as a drawing or specimen) and their order. Flashcards of specific insects and of whole orders may be used here.

3. Quiz (if applicable).

Order Facts

Recite the facts for the order, and emphasize them as the core of the lesson.

Reading and Questions

1. Read aloud from the assigned text in the lesson.

2. Answer questions as a class or individually. Check the students' answers.

Observation and Sketching

1. Observe similarities among the insects.

2. Observe differences. Students may add notes beside each insect, marking its unique features.

3. Analyze the insects' main shapes, and then students draw one or more of them.

Activities

1. Extra reading may begin after drawings are completed. Students will answer questions about the reading for homework.

2. Other activities to do at home may be included.

UNIT I
What Are Insects?

Lesson 1: What Is an Insect?

Insect Facts

- Animal with body made of rings
- 3 parts: head, thorax, and abdomen
- Six legs
- Two or four wings

Reading and Questions

Insects Reader pp. 5-8

1. How much of the animal kingdom is made up of insects? __Three-fourths of the animal kingdom is made up of insects.__

2. Name five different kinds of insects from the reading. __e.g., cabbage butterfly, red admiral, aphis, lady-bird, rose-beetle, grasshopper, etc.__

3. How many parts make up an insect's body? __three__

4. What are the body parts called? __head, thorax, and abdomen__

5. From the tail of the insect to its head, it is divided into what? __rings__

6. How does an insect breathe air? __through breathing holes along the sides of its body__

7. Why is a crane fly, or daddy-longlegs, different from other insects like bees, butterflies, and beetles? __It has two wings, not four.__

8. What do you need to remember about insects? __They have six legs; their body is divided into three parts; you can see rings in their hind body or abdomen; their legs and wings grow on the front body or thorax; they never breathe through their mouths; and while bees, butterflies, and beetles have four wings, flies have two wings and two stumps.__

Observation and Sketching

- Let's take a common insect, the grasshopper, and study the parts of its body. Look at the picture of the grasshopper below and label its parts as you read. The first part, the head (A), is labeled for you.
- On the head are the antennae (D) and eyes (E). Also on the head is the mouth.
- In the middle of the body is the thorax (B). On the thorax are the forelegs (F), hind legs (G), and forewings (H). The legs have joints that work like your elbow and knee. The forewings usually cover the hind wings when at rest.
- The last part, the abdomen (C), has spiracles (I) and an ovipositor (J). Spiracles are holes on the sides of the body used for breathing. Air enters an insect's body not through a nose, but through spiracles. The ovipositor is used to lay eggs, and for some insects (e.g., wasp, honeybee) it is also a stinger.

Insect Body Parts

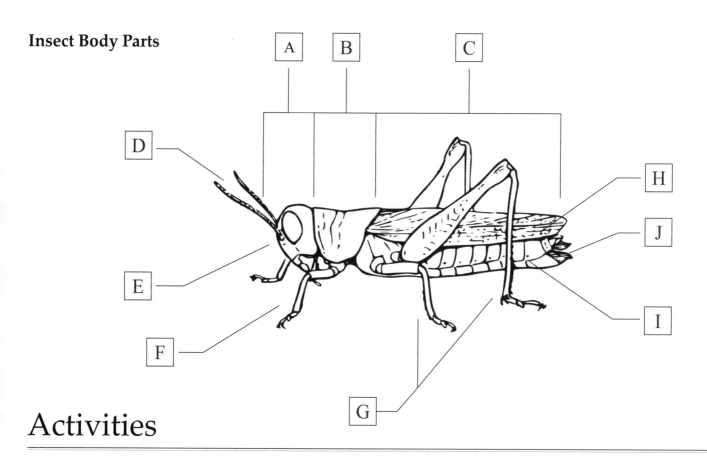

Activities

1. Recite from memory the **Insect Facts** at the beginning of this lesson.
2. In your yard or a park, look for insects and try to identify their parts.

Lesson 2: Insects and Other Animals

Arthropod Facts

- Living things are classified in these groups: *Kingdom, Phylum, Class, Order, Family, Genus, Species.*

- Insects belong with other similar animals in the Phylum called *Arthropods*.

- Arthropods have jointed legs, an exoskeleton, and a segmented body.

- Arthropod classes are separated by how many legs they have: *Insects* (6), *Arachnids* (8), *Crustaceans* (10), *centipedes* (a lot), and *millipedes* (a whole lot).

Reading and Questions

Insects Reader pp. 8-11

1. What are animals made to fit? __They are made to fit the place where they live.__

2. What does "Arthropod" mean? __It means "jointed legs."__

3. What is another feature of an Arthropod's body besides jointed legs? _____
   They have a hard outer skin, or exoskeleton.

4. What kinds of Arthropods are crabs and lobsters? __They are Crustaceans.__

5. Give some examples of Arachnids. __Arachnids include spiders, scorpions, and ticks.__

6. What two classes of Arthropods have many legs running down their long body? __These are__ centipedes and millipedes.

7. How do we tell Arthropods apart? __We tell them apart based on how many legs they have.__

8. How many legs does each class of Arthropods have? __Insects have six legs, Arachnids eight,__ Crustaceans ten, centipedes a lot, and millipedes a whole lot.

Observation and Sketching

- Below is a circle of Arthropods. Analyze the animals by looking at their body parts. The most important question to ask about each one is, "How many legs does it have?"
- Compare the animals with each other. Which ones are similar, or have the same number of legs? Circle all the Arachnids in blue, the Crustaceans in brown, millipedes and centipedes in yellow, and insects in red.
- Contrast the groups. In what ways—apart from the number of legs—do they differ?

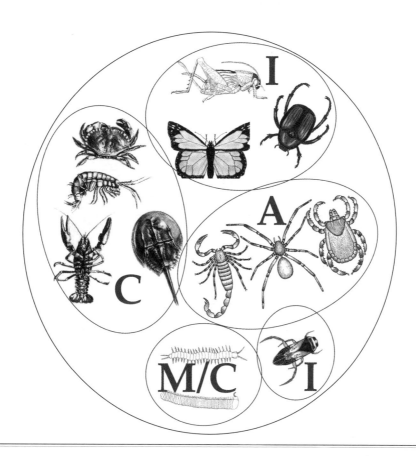

Activities

1. Recite from memory the **Arthropod Facts** at the beginning of this lesson.
2. Review the **Facts** from Lesson 1. Search for Arthropods in your yard, and try to tell which class they belong to.

Lesson 3: Different Orders of Insects

Class Facts

- The class called "Insects" is divided into Orders.
- The Orders are defined by the shape of their body parts.

- The eight Orders in this book are: Odonata, Orthoptera, Dictyoptera, Hemiptera, Diptera, Coleoptera, Lepidoptera, Hymenoptera.

Reading and Questions

Insects Reader pp. 11-15

1. How many insects do scientists guess there are? They guess 30 million.

2. Insects are separated into groups based on characteristics. What are these groups called?
   They are called orders.

3. What insects are in Order Odonata? The dragonfly and damselfly are in this order.

4. In what order do the insects have strong hind legs for jumping? Order Orthoptera

5. What is special about the wings of insects in Order Hemiptera? The first half of the wing is rough, but the tip is smooth.

6. How many wings do flies have? They have two wings.

7. Name two insects from Order Coleoptera. Examples: ladybug, firefly, ground beetle, whirligig beetle, Japanese beetle, and sweet potato weevil

8. What does "Lepidoptera" mean? It means "scaly wings."

9. Do social insects like bees live together? Yes.

Observation and Sketching

- Compare the insects in each Order with each other. For example, what is similar about the insects in Order Odonata, dragonflies and damselflies?
- Contrast the Orders. What is different about them? For example, how are insects in Order Diptera different from those in Order Lepidoptera?

Odonata	Orthoptera	Dictyoptera	Hemiptera	Diptera	Coleoptera	Lepidoptera	Hymenoptera

- Recite the eight Orders of insects with their scientific and common names, kind of metamorphosis, and two main traits/characteristics:

  Odonata (toothed) — Dragonflies and Damselflies; incomplete metamorphosis; water nymphs and needle-like abdomen

  Orthoptera (straight-winged) — Grasshoppers and Crickets; incomplete metamorphosis; fan-like hind wings and leathery front wings

  Dictyoptera (net-winged) — Cockroaches and Mantids; incomplete metamorphosis; fan-like hind wings and leathery front wings

  Hemiptera (half-winged) — True Bugs; incomplete metamorphosis; first half of wing is rough and tip is smooth

  Diptera (two-winged) — Flies; complete metamorphosis; soft body and sucking mouthparts

  Coleoptera (sheath-winged) — Beetles; complete metamorphosis; front wings are hard and meet down the middle of the back

  Lepidoptera (scale-winged) — Butterflies and Moths; complete metamorphosis; large wings and coiling mouthparts

  Hymenoptera (membrane-winged) — Bees, Wasps, and Ants; complete metamorphosis; slender waist and stingers

Activities

1. Recite from memory the **Class Facts** at the beginning of this lesson.
2. Review the **Facts** from Lessons 1 and 2.

Lesson 4: What is Metamorphosis?

Metamorphosis Facts

- Metamorphosis is how insects grow
- Two kinds: incomplete and complete
- Incomplete: egg, nymph, adult
- Complete: egg, larva, pupa, adult

Reading and Questions

Insects Reader pp. 15-17

1. What do we call the special way that insects grow? It is called metamorphosis.

2. What does "metamorphosis" mean? It means a change in shape.

3. What are the two different ways that insects can grow? They can grow by complete or incomplete metamorphosis.

4. What are the three stages of incomplete metamorphosis? The stages are egg, nymph, and adult.

5. Name an insect that grows by incomplete metamorphosis. example: the dragonfly

6. What are the four stages of complete metamorphosis? The stages are egg, larva, pupa, and adult.

7. What stage of complete metamorphosis is worm-like? It is the larva stage.

8. What are two names of insect larvae? examples: caterpillar, grub, maggot

9. What do we call the case made of silk that an insect wraps around its body in complete metamorphosis? It is a pupa.

Observation and Sketching

- Compare incomplete and complete metamorphosis. How are they alike?
- Contrast them and find their differences.
- Analyze the stages of each, and then label the spaces with: egg, nymph, larva, pupa, or adult.

Incomplete Metamorphosis

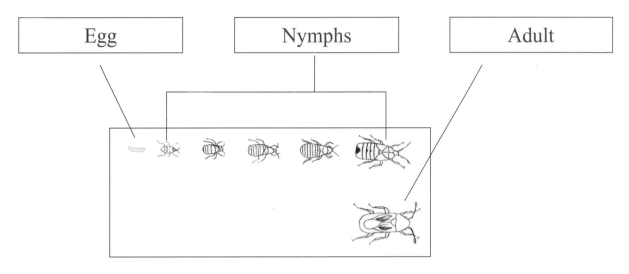

Complete Metamorphosis

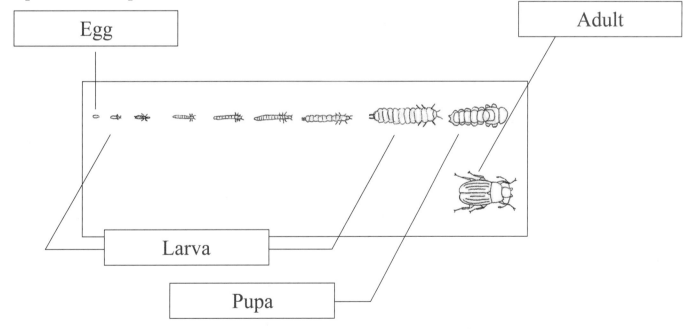

Activities

1. Read pp. 17-20, "Parts of a Caterpillar," in the *Insects Reader*, and then answer this question: How many "true legs" does a caterpillar have? <u>A caterpillar has six "true legs."</u>
2. Recite from memory the **Metamorphosis Facts** at the beginning of this lesson. Then recite the **Facts** from Lessons 1-3.

Lesson 5: Unit I Review

Unit I Facts

- The following fill-in-the-blank and short-answer questions will test your mastery of the facts learned from each lesson in Unit I.

Insect Facts

1. Insects are animals with a body made of ___rings___ .
2. Insects have three main body parts, which are the ___head, thorax, and abdomen___ .
3. How many legs do all insects have? ___six___
4. How many wings do most insects have? ___two or four___

Arthropod Facts

1. Into what groups are living things classified? ___Kingdom, Phylum, Class, Order, Family, Genus, Species___
2. Insects belong with other similar animals in which group? ___Arthropods___
3. What three characteristics do all Arthropods have? ___jointed legs, segmented body, exoskeleton___
4. Arthropod classes are separated by how many legs they have: ___Insects (6), Arachnids (8), Crustaceans (10), Centipedes (a lot), Millipedes (a whole lot)___

Class Facts

1. The class called "Insects" is divided into ___orders___ .
2. The Orders are separated by the shape of their ___body parts___ .
3. The eight Orders in this book are ___Odonata, Orthoptera, Dictyoptera, Hemiptera, Diptera, Coleoptera, Lepidoptera, Hymenoptera___ .

Metamorphosis Facts

1. Metamorphosis is how insects _____grow_____ .
2. What are two kinds of metamorphosis? _____incomplete and complete_____
3. What are the stages in incomplete metamorphosis? _____egg, nymph, adult_____
4. What are the stages in complete metamorphosis? _____egg, larva, pupa, adult_____

Unit I Reading

- The following multiple-choice questions are from the reading questions in the lessons of Unit I. Circle the correct answer.

1. How much of the animal kingdom is made up of insects?   (¼, ½, ¾)
2. How many parts make up an insect's body?   (2, 3, 4)
3. Arthropods are divided into classes based on their: (size, legs, wings)
4. How many legs do Arachnids have?   (4, 6, 8)
5. How many kinds of insects do scientists think exist?   (30, 300, 30 million)
6. How many wings do flies have?   (2, 4, 6)
7. How many stages are in incomplete metamorphosis?   (3, 4, 5)
8. How many stages are in complete metamorphosis?   (3, 4, 5)

Activities

1. Recite from memory the **Facts** from the lessons in Unit I.
2. Review Lessons 1-4, especially the **Observation and Sketching** sections.

UNIT II
Odonata, Orthoptera, Dictyoptera, and Hemiptera

Lesson 6: Odonata I

Order Facts

- Odonata [Greek: οδοντος] means "toothed"
- Dragonflies and Damselflies
- Incomplete metamorphosis
- Characteristics: water nymphs and needle-like abdomen

Reading and Questions

Insects Reader pp. 21-26

1. Why are dragonflies not easy to catch? They are swift and shy.

2. What other insects are "cousins" of the dragonfly? They are termites, may-flies, and lace-wing flies.

3. Describe the dragonfly's wings. They are large, fine, lace-like wings, divided into spaces. They are equal in size.

4. Describe the dragonfly's body, or abdomen. It is long and thin.

5. Where may dragonflies be found? They live in wet places like lakes, ponds, marshy places, or quiet streams.

6. What does the mother dragonfly do with her eggs? She drops her eggs on the water, or she may put them into plant stems.

7. What is the dragonfly nymph's way of catching food like? It is like a person with a net catching insects.

8. How is a dragonfly nymph like a steamboat? It moves forward by shooting water behind it.

9. What happens to the dragonfly as time gets nearer for it to come out of the water as an adult? Its case grows clearer, its eyes brighter, and it leaves the deeper part of the water and gets near the edge.

Observation and Sketching

- Compare these parts of the dragonfly nymph and adult: legs, head, abdomen. How are they alike?
- Contrast these parts: thorax, abdomen, head. How are they different?
- Analyze the main parts of the adult dragonfly (i.e., head, thorax, abdomen, wings, legs), and then draw your own version of the adult in the space below.

Dragonfly Nymph **Adult Dragonfly**

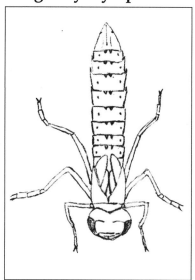 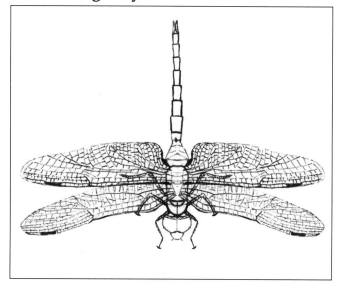

Activities

1. Read pp. 26-28, "The Dragonfly and His Companions," in the *Insects Reader*, and answer the following question: What are the dragonfly's wings covered with?
   They are covered with cross-bars filled with air.

2. Recite from memory the **Facts** you have learned about Order Odonata.

3. Make flashcards for each insect. Write the name of the insect on one side and facts about it on the other. You could also draw a small picture on one side.

Lesson 7: Odonata II

Order Facts

- Odonata [Greek: οδοντος] means "toothed"
- Dragonflies and Damselflies
- Incomplete metamorphosis
- Characteristics: water nymphs and needle-like abdomen

Reading and Questions

Insects Reader pp. 28-36

1. What does the dragonfly nymph climb to leave the water? It climbs a tall reed or grass that grows in the water.

2. What kinds of food does the dragonfly eat as an adult? It eats beetles, spiders, flies, centipedes, fresh-water shrimps, and polliwogs.

3. What part of the dragonfly is like "two great flaming jewels"? The eyes are the flaming jewels.

4. What are the Darning-Needle and Ringed-Club? They are two types of dragonflies.

5. The reading calls the damselfly by another name. What is it? It is called the Little Lady.

6. Describe the damselfly's color and wings. The damselfly is sometimes bright red or clear light blue. They are small, like fairies.

7. Why should you never try to help a dragonfly out of its case? Its wings would be ruined and never take the right shape.

8. What goes through the tiny tubes that make up the frame of the dragonfly's wings? Air and blood is pumped through them.

9. What does air and blood pumping through the wings' frame help do? It spreads out the wings and body of the dragonfly.

Observation and Sketching

- Compare these parts of the dragonfly and damselfly: wings and abdomen. How are they alike?
- Contrast their wings, head, and size. How are they different?
- Analyze the main parts of the damselfly, and then draw your own version of it in the space below.

Adult Damselfly

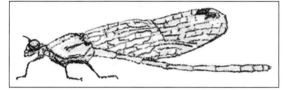

Adult Dragonfly

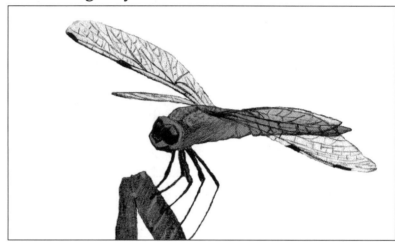

Activities

1. Read pp. 36-38, "Down Below," in the *Insects Reader*, and answer the following question:

   When trying to net dragonfly nymphs, what other creatures might you find?

   e.g., little fish, water snails, tadpoles, caddis-worm, grubs of gnats and mayflies

2. Recite from memory the **Facts** you have learned about Order Odonata.

Lesson 8: Orthoptera and Dictyoptera I

Order Facts

- Orthoptera [Greek: ορθο + πτερα] means "straight-winged"; Dictyoptera [Greek: δικτυον + πτερα] means "net-winged"
- Orthoptera: Grasshoppers, crickets, and katydids (also includes locusts)

- Dictyoptera: cockroaches and mantids
- Incomplete metamorphosis
- Characteristics: fan-like hind wings and leathery front wings

Reading and Questions

Insects Reader pp. 38-45

1. What is the curious long tube at the end of the female grasshopper's body?
   It is an egg-layer that she forces into the ground to lay her eggs.

2. How do crickets and grasshoppers make their chirping sound? They rub their wings together.

3. Why is a field cricket very useful in the garden? He feeds on insects, sitting outside his hole at night to catch them.

4. What kind of cricket does mischief in the garden by tunneling and eating roots and stems?
   The mole cricket does this mischief.

5. What insects in this order eat everything they can get and have a repulsive smell? This insect is the cockroach.

6. Who is "the old man of the meadow"? It is the grasshopper.

7. What is the "splendid dress coat under his sober overcoat"? It is the grasshopper's wings.

8. Orthopterans are called straight-wings because they do not fold their wings in what way?
   They do not fold their wings crosswise.

9. Give an example of each: a runner, a snatcher, and a jumper. Some examples are cockroach, mantid, and grasshopper.

10. Do grasshoppers prefer to eat plant or animal food? Grasshoppers prefer plant food.

Observation and Sketching

- Compare these parts of the grasshopper and cricket: legs, abdomen, head, antennae. How are they alike?
- Contrast their abdomens and color. How are they different?
- Analyze the main parts of the cockroach, and then draw your own version of it in the space below.

Cricket

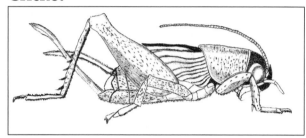

Cockroach

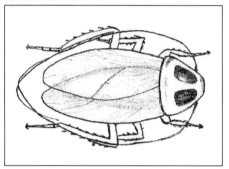

Grasshopper

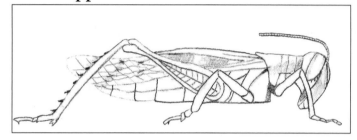

Activities

1. Read pp. 45-50, "The Robber Cousin," in the *Insects Reader*, and answer the following question: Who is the "Robber Cousin"? ___It is the locust.___
2. Recite from memory the **Facts** you have learned about Orders Odonata, Orthoptera, and Dictyoptera.

Lesson 9: Orthoptera and Dictyoptera II

Order Facts

- Orthoptera [Greek: ορθο + πτερα] means "straight-winged"; Dictyoptera [Greek: δικτυον + πτερα] means "net-winged"
- Orthoptera: Grasshoppers, crickets, and katydids (also includes locusts)

- Dictyoptera: cockroaches and mantids
- Incomplete metamorphosis
- Characteristics: fan-like hind wings and leathery front wings

Reading and Questions

Insects Reader pp. 50-57

1. What does the mother grasshopper use her "sword" for? _____ She uses it to dig a hole in the ground and lay eggs in the hole.

2. When grasshopper larvae hatch from the egg, do they look like the adult parent? Yes, but they are smaller and have no wings.

3. Are the grasshopper's wing cases and body ring hard like a shell or like tough skin? _____ They are like tough skin.

4. How long is the wart biter grasshopper? It is nearly two inches long.

5. What kills the grasshopper? _____ Frost and cold kill it in winter.

6. Is the cricket's body slender like the grasshopper or short and thick? _____ It is short and thick.

7. What color is the cricket? It is dark, glossy brown.

8. What does the cricket have to tell him of danger behind? He has a pair of long, stiff tail hairs.

9. Give an example of what a cricket might drink and eat. e.g., A cricket might drink water, milk, soup, tea, beer, vinegar, yeast; a cricket might eat bread crumbs, grease, meat, small insects, leather, woolen cloth, stockings, clothes.

10. Where does the field cricket make his house? He makes his house in the earth.

Observation and Sketching

- Compare these parts of the katydid and mantid: wings, hind legs, and color. How are they alike?
- Contrast these parts and find their differences: forelegs, head, antennae.
- Analyze the three main parts of the mantid, and then draw your own version of it in the space below.

Mantid

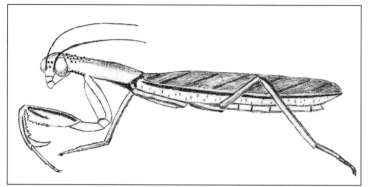

Katydid

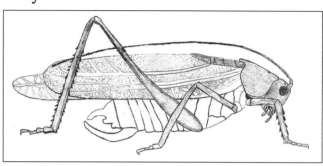

Activities

1. Read pp. 58-60, "A Queer Cricket," in the *Insects Reader*, and answer the following question:
   Who is the "Queer Cricket"? _____ It is the mole cricket. _____
2. Recite from memory the **Facts** you have learned about Orders Odonata, Orthoptera, and Dictyoptera.

Lesson 10: Hemiptera I

Order Facts

- Hemiptera [Greek: ημι + πτερα] means "half-winged"
- Water bugs, hoppers
- Incomplete metamorphosis

- Characteristics: first half of wing is rough but the tip is smooth
- Also includes: cicadas, aphids, and other "true bugs"

Reading and Questions

Insects Reader pp. 60-62

1. How does the "water measurer" get its name? He seems to measure the water with his legs as he runs.

2. What does the water measurer have under his body and on his legs that keeps him from getting wet and sinking? He has very fine hairs.

3. How does the "water scorpion" get its name? His front legs are thick and strong, with pincers at the end.

4. What does the water scorpion use his pincers for? He uses these pincers to seize insects in the water, and sucks them dry through his sharp beak.

5. In the United States, the greater water boatman is called the "backswimmer." Why is it called this name? He swims upside down, rowing himself along with these two legs as if they were oars.

6. What is similar about the way the backswimmer and the other two water bugs eat insects? They bite them with their sharp beaks and suck out their soft bodies.

7. Where do water bugs lay eggs? The eggs are laid on stems and leaves in the water.

Observation and Sketching

- Compare the wings of the water measurer and backswimmer. How are they alike?
- Contrast the legs and shape of their body. How are they different?
- Analyze the main parts of the water measurer, and then draw your own version of it in the space below.

Water Measurer

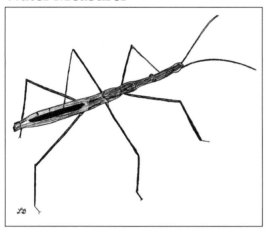

Backswimmer

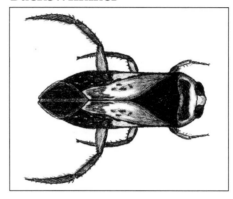

Activities

1. Continue making flashcards for each insect you have studied so far.
2. Recite from memory the **Facts** you have learned about Orders Odonata, Orthoptera, and Dictyoptera.

Lesson 11: Hemiptera II

Order Facts

- Hemiptera [Greek: ημι + πτερα] means "half-winged"
- Water bugs, hoppers
- Incomplete metamorphosis
- Characteristics: first half of wing is rough but the tip is smooth
- Also includes: cicadas, aphids, and other "true bugs"

Reading and Questions

Insects Reader pp. 62-65

1. What made the balls of foam on the blades of grass? __Hoppers, or frog-hoppers__

2. How did the hopper use the sap from the grass that made the foam? __He used it for food and to make the foam cloak for safety and warmth.__

3. Who is the frog-hopper's small cousin that spoils roses and is the ant's cow? __It is the aphis, or aphid.__

4. Who is the biggest cousin of the frog-hopper? __It is the cicada.__

5. Why are hoppers not good friends of plants like bees and ants are? __They make plants sickly by sucking out the sap.__

6. What is called "the singer," "the screamer," and "the squealer"? __It is the cicada.__

7. Where does Mrs. Cicada bore holes for her eggs? __She bores the holes in trees.__

8. When will people say, "Ah, now it will be hot and dry"? __They say this in mid-summer, when the shrill song of the cicada is heard.__

Observation and Sketching

- Compare the abdomens of the cicada, leaf-hopper, and aphid. How else are they alike?
- Contrast their wings, and find other differences.
- Analyze the parts of the leaf-hopper, and then draw your own version of it in the space below.

Cicada

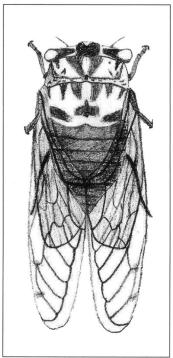

Leaf-hopper

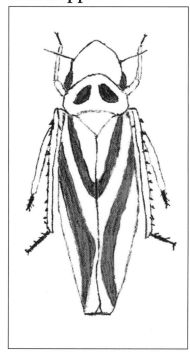

Aphid

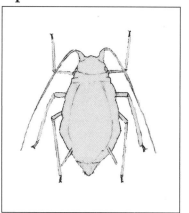

Activities

1. Study your flashcards and make new ones for the insects above.
2. Recite from memory the **Facts** you have learned about Orders Odonata, Orthoptera, and Dictyoptera.

Lesson 12: Unit II Review

Unit II Facts

Odonata Facts

1. Odonata means ____toothed_____ .
2. What two kinds of insects are in Order Odonata? _____
   ___dragonflies and damselflies_____
3. Insects in Odonata grow by _____incomplete_____ metamorphosis.
4. The characteristics of Order Odonata are ___water nymphs and needle-like abdomen___
   _____ .

Orthoptera and Dictyoptera Facts

1. Orthoptera means ____straight-winged_____ .
2. Dictyoptera means ___net-winged_____ .
3. Order Orthoptera includes grasshoppers, crickets, and ___katydids_____ .
4. Order Dictyoptera includes cockroaches and ____mantids_____ .
5. Insects in these two orders grow by _____incomplete_____ metamorphosis.
6. The characteristics of these two orders are ____fan-like hind wings and leathery front wings___
   _____ .
7. Other insects in Order Orthoptera include _____locusts_____
   _____ .

Hemiptera Facts

1. Hemiptera means _____half-winged_____ .
2. Order Hemiptera includes water bugs and _____hoppers_____ .
3. Insects in Hemiptera grow by _____incomplete_____ metamorphosis.
4. The characteristics of Order Hemiptera are _____first half of wing is rough but the tip is smooth___
   _____ .
5. Other insects in this order include cicadas, aphids, and other _____true bugs_____
   _____ .

Observation and Sketching

- Review the insects from Order Odonata. How are they alike?
- Contrast them and find their differences.
- Analyze the parts of these insects, label them, and then draw a small basic version of them in the space provided.

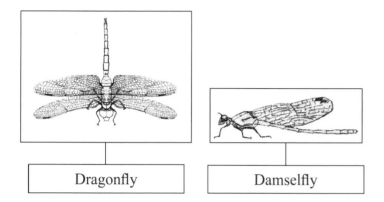

| Dragonfly | Damselfly |

- Review the insects from Order Orthoptera and Order Dictyoptera. How are they alike?
- Contrast them and find their differences.
- Analyze the parts of these insects and label them. Draw two of them below.

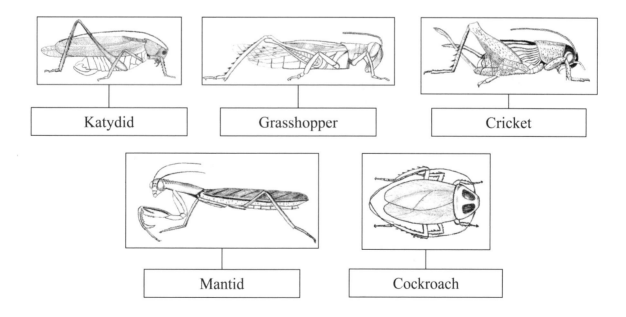

Katydid   Grasshopper   Cricket

Mantid   Cockroach

- Review the insects from Order Hemiptera. How are they alike?
- Contrast them and find their differences.
- Analyze the parts of these insects, and label them. Draw two of them below.

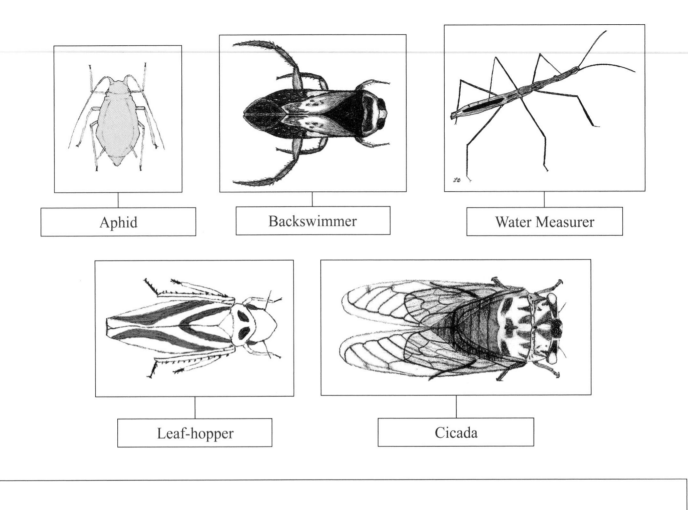

Aphid

Backswimmer

Water Measurer

Leaf-hopper

Cicada

Activities

1. Study your flashcards and all of Unit II. Reread lessons in the textbook.
2. Recite from memory the **Facts** you have learned about Orders Odonata, Orthoptera, Dictyoptera, and Hemiptera.

UNIT III
Diptera and Coleoptera

Lesson 13: Diptera I

Order Facts

- Diptera [Greek: δι + πτερα] means "two-winged"
- House fly, mosquito, crane fly, horse fly, bluebottle
- Complete metamorphosis
- Characteristics: soft body and sucking mouthparts
- Also includes: gnat, midge, fruit fly, bot fly

Reading and Questions

Insects Reader pp. 66-71

1. How are real flies different from other insects called "flies"? Real flies have only two wings.

2. How many eggs does the female house fly lay at a time? She lays 150 eggs at a time.

3. What is the name of a fly larva? It is called a maggot.

4. What are two small flies? The gnat and midge are small flies.

5. What is the farmers' name for the grub of the "daddy-longlegs"?
   They are called "leather jackets."

6. What are the three stages that some insects pass through before becoming an adult?
   The states are the egg, larva, and the pupa.

7. What does the larva of a fly look like? It is a small white worm with rings, and on the rings are hooks.

8. When does a fly grow its legs, wings, and head with mouth, eyes, and trunk?
   It grows these parts while it is a pupa.

Observation and Sketching

- Compare the legs, wings, antennae, and abdomen of the house fly, bluebottle, and horse fly. How are they alike?
- Contrast their heads, body size, and wing shape. How are they different?
- Analyze the parts of the horse fly, and then draw your own version of it in the space below.

House Fly

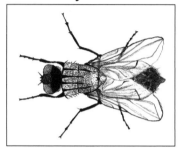

Bluebottle

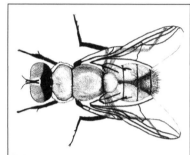

Horse Fly

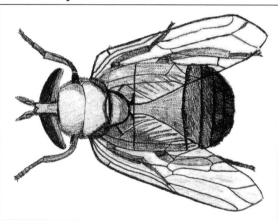

Activities

1. Read pp. 71-73, "Mrs. Fly and Her Foes," of the *Insects Reader*, and answer the following question: Where does Mrs. Fly lay her eggs? <u>She lays eggs in food.</u>
2. Recite from memory the **Facts** you have learned about Orders Odonata, Orthoptera, Dictyoptera, and Diptera.
3. Make new flashcards for the insects above.

Lesson 14: Diptera II

Order Facts

- Diptera [Greek: δι + πτερα] means "two-winged"
- House fly, mosquito, crane fly, horse fly, bluebottle
- Complete metamorphosis
- Characteristics: soft body and sucking mouthparts
- Also includes: gnat, midge, fruit fly, bot fly

Reading and Questions

Insects Reader pp. 73-78

1. Are the eyes of a fly big or small? The eyes are big.

2. What other animal, like the fly, has an upper lip that is a trunk? The elephant's upper lip is a trunk.

3. What do the hairs and pad on a fly's foot act like? They act like a sucker that helps the fly walk upside-down.

4. What is the work of Mrs. Fly? Her work is to lay many eggs in dead things.

5. Why is the work of the fly useful to people? They get rid of small things that would do us harm and cause death and disease.

6. What animals eat flies for food? Many birds, fish, frogs and some insects eat flies.

7. What fly lays eggs that injure trees? It is the gall fly.

8. Which fly "worries" horses by biting them? It is the horse fly.

9. What kind of insect is the "Spanish fly"? The Spanish fly is really a kind of beetle.

Observation and Sketching

- Compare the wings, abdomen, and legs of the mosquito and crane fly. How are they alike?
- Contrast the house fly with the crane fly and mosquito. How is it different?
- Analyze the parts of the mosquito, and then draw your own version of it in the space below.

Mosquito   **Crane Fly**   **House Fly**

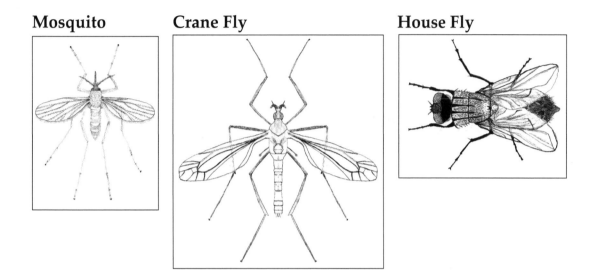

Activities

1. Read pp. 79-80, "A Swarm of Flies," in the *Insects Reader*, and answer the following question: Do flies live together or separately?   They live separately.
2. Recite from memory the **Facts** you have learned about Orders Odonata, Orthoptera, Dictyoptera, and Diptera.

Lesson 15: Coleoptera I

Order Facts

- Coleoptera [Greek: κολεος + πτερα] means "sheath-winged"
- Ladybug, firefly, ground beetle, whirligig beetle, Japanese beetle, sweet potato weevil
- Complete metamorphosis
- Characteristics: front wings are hard and meet down the middle of the back
- Also includes: click beetle, june bug, cocktail, tiger beetle, stag beetle

Reading and Questions

Insects Reader pp. 80-87

1. What class do beetles belong to: eaters or drinkers? Beetles are eaters.

2. How are beetles like "old-time soldiers"? They are covered with a hard, horny shell that is like armor.

3. What are the hard cases over the beetle's back? They are two wings used for armor, but not for flight.

4. Where do female beetles lay eggs? They may lay eggs in earth, water, dead animals, tree holes, or in fruit.

5. What kinds of things do beetle larvae eat? They eat wood, trees, fruit, flowers, meal, furs, clothes, and almost anything but metals.

6. What does the beetle do as a pupa? It can do nothing but wait.

7. Why do beetles receive so much notice? There are very many of them, of many kinds. They live where we can see them. They are easy to take apart and study. They have great beauty.

8. How do beetles breathe? They breathe through pipes or tubes wound all over the body.

9. What are some colors that beetles may be? They may be brown, black, red, green, or golden.

Observation and Sketching

- Compare the forewings and legs of the ladybug, firefly, and ground beetle. How are they alike?
- Contrast their body shape and color.
- Analyze the parts of the ladybug, and then draw your own version of it in the space below.

Ladybug   **Firefly**   **Ground Beetle**

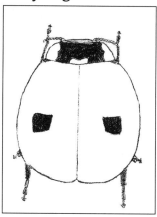 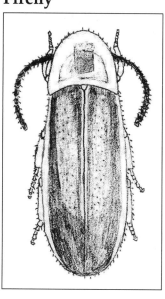 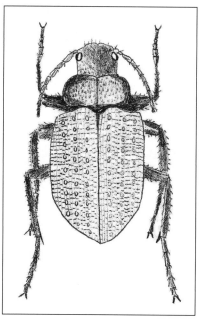

Activities

1. Read pp. 87-90, "Injurious Beetles," of the *Insects Reader,* and answer the following question: What kind of beetle can flip? ____It is the click beetle.____

2. Recite from memory the **Facts** you have learned about Orders Odonata, Orthoptera, Dictyoptera, Diptera, and Coleoptera.

3. Make new flashcards and study them all.

Lesson 16: Coleoptera II

Order Facts

- Coleoptera [Greek: κολεος + πτερα] means "sheath-winged"
- Ladybug, firefly, ground beetle, whirligig beetle, Japanese beetle, sweet potato weevil
- Complete metamorphosis
- Characteristics: front wings are hard and meet down the middle of the back
- Also includes: click beetle, june bug, cocktail, tiger beetle, stag beetle

Reading and Questions

Insects Reader pp. 90-98

1. Which beetle has long, slender legs, moves fast, and is fierce and cunning?
   It is the tiger beetle.

2. What does a tiger beetle grub dig a tunnel for? It waits in the tunnel for insects to pass by, so that it can catch them for food.

3. What insects seldom fly but are the best hunters? They are the ground beetles.

4. Why is a ladybug a useful beetle? It eats plant bugs and aphids that destroy our plants.

5. What weapon does the stag beetle have? It has very large, strong jaws, and can give a good pinch.

6. How do beetles in the "Oil family" defend themselves? They drop oil that smells bad and blisters skin.

7. Which beetles live in hot lands and are scarce? The answer is very large beetles.

8. What part of the stag beetle is like a "plume of six feathers"? This part is its feelers.

9. What are male stag beetles fond of doing? They like fighting with each other.

Observation and Sketching

- Compare the legs and wings of the tiger beetle, Japanese beetle, and sweet potato weevil. How are they alike?
- Contrast their body size, shape, color, and antennae.
- Analyze the parts of the Japanese beetle, and then draw your own version of it in the space below.

Tiger Beetle

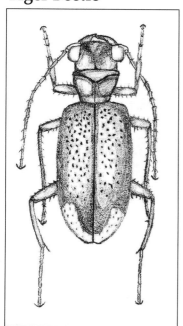

Japanese Beetle

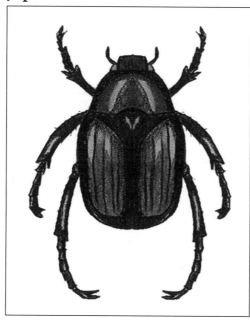

Sweet Potato Weevil

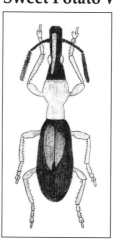

Activities

1. Read pp. 98-100, "The Rose Beetle," of the *Insects Reader*, and answer the following question: What color is the rose beetle? ___It is a rich golden green.___

2. Recite from memory the **Facts** you have learned about Orders Odonata, Orthoptera, Dictyoptera, Diptera, and Coleoptera.

Lesson 17: Coleoptera III

Order Facts

- Coleoptera [Greek: κολεος + πτερα] means "sheath-winged"
- Ladybug, firefly, ground beetle, whirligig beetle, Japanese beetle, sweet potato weevil
- Complete metamorphosis

- Characteristics: front wings are hard and meet down the middle of the back
- Also Includes: click beetle, june bug, cocktail, tiger beetle, stag beetle

Reading and Questions

Insects Reader pp. 101-107

1. Why is one kind of beetle called "short-coat"?   It has short wing-cases.

2. What two insects sometimes share their home with short-coat beetles?
   These insects are termites and ants.

3. How are water beetles built like a boat?   The parts of their bodies fit closely to form a water-tight case.

4. How are water beetles' bodies shaped?   They are shaped like a fish or boat.

5. For what are the long legs of water beetles used?   They are used for swimming.

6. For what might a water beetle use the thorn on his breast?   It is used to poke someone who picks it up.

7. Where does a water beetle keep air when it is under water?   It keeps air under its wing-covers.

8. What is the water beetle that spins round and round?   It is the whirligig beetle.

9. Do whirligig beetles live in quiet water or swift water?   They live in ponds or very quiet streams.

Observation and Sketching

- Compare the front wings and body shape of the firefly, ground beetle, and whirligig beetle. How are they alike?
- Contrast their size, antennae, and other differences.
- Analyze the parts of the firefly, and then draw your own version of it in the space below.

Firefly

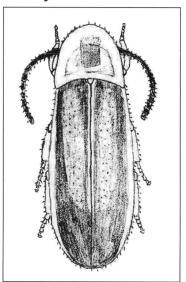

Ground Beetle

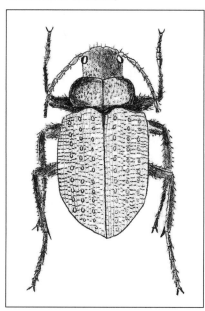

Whirligig Beetle

Activities

1. Read pp. 108-111, "The Little Sexton," of the *Insects Reader*, and answer the following question: What does a sexton beetle do with dead animals? ___It buries them.___

2. Recite from memory the **Facts** you have learned about Orders Odonata, Orthoptera, Dictyoptera, Diptera, and Coleoptera.

3. Make new flashcards and study old ones.

Lesson 18: Unit III Review

Unit III Facts

Diptera Facts

1. Diptera means ___two-winged___ .
2. Order Diptera includes the house fly, crane fly, horse fly, and ___bluebottle___ .
3. Insects in Diptera grow by ___complete___ metamorphosis.
4. The characteristics of Order Diptera are ___soft body and sucking mouthparts___ .
5. Other insects in this order include the gnat, midge, fruit fly, and ___bot fly___ .

Coleoptera Facts

1. Coleoptera means ___sheath-winged___ .
2. Order Coleoptera includes the ladybug, firefly, ground beetle, ___whirligig beetle, Japanese beetle,___ ___and sweet potato weevil___ .
3. Insects in Coleoptera grow by ___complete___ metamorphosis.
4. The characteristics of Order Coleoptera are ___front wings are hard and meet down the middle___ ___of the back___ .
5. Other insects in this order include the click beetle, june bug, cocktail, tiger beetle, and ___stag beetle___ .

Unit III Reading

- The following multiple choice questions are from the reading questions in the lessons of Unit III. Circle the correct answer.

1. What is the name of a fly larva? (egg, worm, (maggot))

2. Mrs. Fly lays her eggs in: (water, hair, (dead things))

3. The hard cases over the beetle's back are: ((wings,) eggs)

4. This beetle is fast and fierce: (ladybug, (tiger beetle,) firefly)

5. This water beetle spins round and round: ((whirligig,) ground beetle, Japanese beetle)

Observation and Sketching

- Review the insects from Order Diptera. How are they alike?
- Contrast them and find their differences.
- Analyze the parts of the insects, and label them.

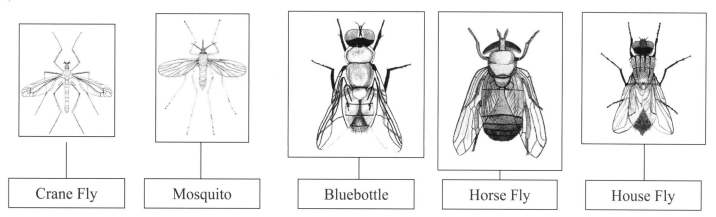

| Crane Fly | Mosquito | Bluebottle | Horse Fly | House Fly |

- Review the insects from Order Coleoptera. How are they alike?
- Contrast them and find their differences.
- Analyze the parts of the beetles, and label them.

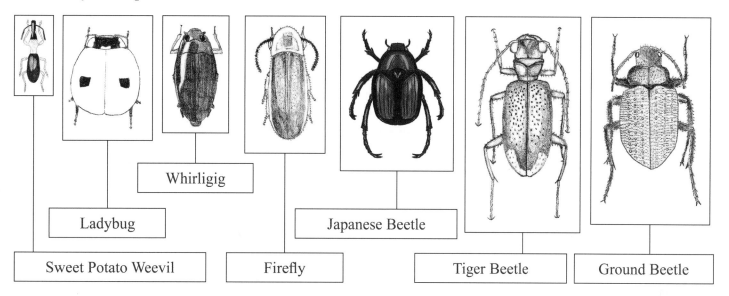

Whirligig

Ladybug

Japanese Beetle

Sweet Potato Weevil

Firefly

Tiger Beetle

Ground Beetle

Activities

1. Study your flashcards and all of Unit III. Reread lessons in the textbook.
2. Recite from memory the **Facts** you have learned about Orders Diptera and Coleoptera.

UNIT IV
Lepidoptera

Order Facts

- Lepidoptera [Greek: λεπιδος + πτερα] means "scale-winged"
- Cabbage butterfly, sphinx moth, monarch butterfly, brush-footed butterfly, swallowtail butterfly, luna moth
- Complete metamorphosis

- Characteristics: large wings and coiling mouthparts
- Also includes: tiger moth, cecropia moth, skipper butterfly

Reading and Questions

Insects Reader pp. 111-118

1. What family does the moth belong to—the "club-horns" or "varied-horns"? The moth belongs to the "varied-horns."

2. Do all moths do harm by eating clothes? No, only some damage clothes by eating them.

3. What other flying animal does the hawk moth seem to fly like? It flies like the humming bird or the swallow*.

4. What is another name for the moth caterpillar that makes silk? It is the silk worm.

5. When a moth caterpillar gets ready to start its pupa stage, what does it spin around itself? It spins a cocoon.

6. What attracts moths that fly at night? They are attracted to light.

7. Do moths have soft bodies or hard? They have soft bodies.

*See p. 112: "It was hard to distinguish him from a hummingbird. Then, as he dashed across a moonlit space, he looked like the swallows we had watched at sunset."

Observation and Sketching

- Compare the wings and antennae of the luna moth and sphinx moth. How are they alike?
- Contrast their thorax, abdomen, and the color and markings on their body. How are they different?
- Analyze the parts of the luna moth, and then draw your own version of it in the space below.

Luna Moth

Sphinx Moth

Activities

1. Recite from memory the **Facts** you have learned about Orders Odonata, Orthoptera, Dictyoptera, Diptera, Coleoptera, and Lepidoptera (Moths only).
2. Make new flashcards and study old ones.

Lesson 20: Moths II

Order Facts

- Lepidoptera [Greek: λεπιδος + πτερα] means "scale-winged"
- Cabbage butterfly, sphinx moth, monarch butterfly, brush-footed butterfly, swallowtail butterfly, luna moth
- Complete metamorphosis
- Characteristics: large wings and coiling mouthparts
- Also includes: tiger moth, cecropia moth, skipper butterfly

Reading and Questions

Insects Reader pp. 119-122

1. What does a moth use to get honey from a flower? __It uses its tiny trunk.__

2. What are arranged like "tiles on a roof"? __The scales of a moth's wings are arranged like tiles on a roof.__

3. What are the eyes of a moth shaped like? __They are shaped like "two glorious globes" on each side of its head.__

4. What is the difference between a moth's feelers and a butterfly's? __A moth's feelers are feathery and pointed at the end, but a butterfly's feelers are thin and round at the end.__

5. How does a moth hold its wings when it is not flying, or at rest? __It lays its wings back like a roof on a house.__

6. What is a "wooly bear"? __It is the caterpillar of the tiger moth. It has a hairy body and curls up in a ball if touched.__

7. If you capture a caterpillar, what should be put in its cage? __A piece of the plant it feeds on should be kept with it.__

Observation and Sketching

- Compare the wings, legs, and antennae of the sphinx moth and monarch butterfly. How are they alike?
- Contrast their thorax, abdomen, antennae, and their color and markings.
- Analyze the parts of the sphinx moth, and then draw your own version of it in the space below.

Monarch Butterfly

Sphinx Moth

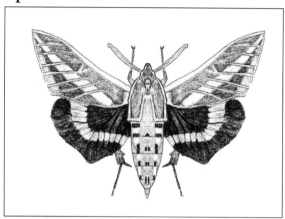

Activities

1. Recite from memory the **Facts** you have learned about Orders Odonata, Orthoptera, Dictyoptera, Diptera, Coleoptera, and Lepidoptera (Moths only).
2. Make new flashcards and study old ones.

Lesson 21: Butterflies I

Order Facts

- Lepidoptera [Greek: λεπιδος + πτερα] means "scale-winged"
- Cabbage butterfly, sphinx moth, monarch butterfly, brush-footed butterfly, swallowtail butterfly, luna moth
- Complete metamorphosis
- Characteristics: large wings and coiling mouthparts
- Also includes: tiger moth, cecropia moth, skipper butterfly

Reading and Questions

Insects Reader pp. 122-128

1. What are the "two fine jewels," the "coiled-up spring of a fairy watch," and the "four lovely fans in black and gold"? _They are leftover parts of a butterfly._

2. Why was the bird able to get the butterfly? _The butterfly was either laying its eggs on a leaf or had already died._

3. What is on the end of a butterfly's "horns"? _A knob is on the end of its horns, or antennae._

4. Does the butterfly have a coat of hairs on its body? _Yes, it does have a coat of hairs._

5. What is coiled up like a watch spring when not in use? _The butterfly's mouth, or trunk, coils up when not in use._

6. On what kind of plants might a butterfly lay its eggs? _It may lay its eggs on an oak, carrot, or cabbage._

7. What colors are on a swallowtail when it is a caterpillar? _It is bright green, with black bands and yellow spots._

8. What does a butterfly do to crack open its pupa case? _It breathes hard._

Observation and Sketching

- Compare the monarch butterfly, swallowtail butterfly, and cabbage butterfly. How are they alike?
- Contrast them and find their differences.
- Analyze the parts of the swallowtail butterfly, and then draw your own version of it in the space below.

Swallowtail Butterfly

Monarch Butterfly

Cabbage Butterfly

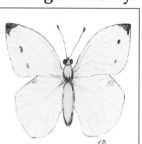

Activities

1. Read pp. 128-132, "Familiar Butterflies," of the *Insects Reader* and answer the following question: What is a butterfly pupa called? _____It is called a chrysalis._____

2. Recite from memory the **Facts** you have learned about Orders Odonata, Orthoptera, Dictyoptera, Diptera, Coleoptera, and Lepidoptera (Moths & Butterflies).

Lesson 22: Butterflies II

Order Facts

- Lepidoptera [Greek: λεπιδος + πτερα] means "scale-winged"
- Cabbage butterfly, sphinx moth, monarch butterfly, brush-footed butterfly, swallowtail butterfly, luna moth
- Complete metamorphosis
- Characteristics: large wings and coiling mouthparts
- Also includes: tiger moth, cecropia moth, skipper butterfly

Reading and Questions

Insects Reader pp. 132-139

1. When a caterpillar hatches, what does it eat? __It eats the plant on which it was laid.__

2. Why might a caterpillar not eat the mid-vein of a leaf? __The vein may be too hard or it may be__ the caterpillar's roadway.

3. What does a caterpillar use to make its home on a leaf? __It uses its silk thread.__

4. Do butterflies usually fly in big swarms or in small groups? __They usually fly in small groups.__

5. Monarch butterflies like the milkweed plant. What colors are they? __They are orange and black.__

6. Does a butterfly fly in a line or in a zig-zag? __It flies in a zig-zag.__

7. What is the color of a butterfly usually the same as? __It is the same as the butterfly's home or__ the general flower color of the season.

Observation and Sketching

- Compare the body shape of the brush-footed butterfly and skipper butterfly. How are they alike?
- Contrast their spots and colors, and find other differences.
- Analyze the parts of the cabbage butterfly, and then draw your own version of it in the space below.

Brush-footed Butterfly

Cabbage Butterfly

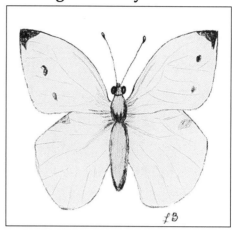

Activities

1. Recite from memory the **Facts** you have learned about Orders Odonata, Orthoptera, Dictyoptera, Diptera, Coleoptera, and Lepidoptera (Moths & Butterflies).
2. Study your flashcards and all of Unit IV. Review lessons in the textbook.

Lesson 23: Unit IV Review

Unit IV Facts

- The following fill-in-the-blank and short-answer questions will test your mastery of the facts learned from each lesson in Unit IV.

Insect Facts

1. Lepidoptera means _____scaled-winged_____ .

2. Order Lepidoptera includes the cabbage butterfly, sphinx moth, monarch butterfly, ____brush-footed butterfly_____, swallowtail butterfly, and _____luna moth_____ .

3. Insects in Lepidoptera grow by _____complete_____ metamorphosis.

4. The characteristics of Order Lepidoptera are____large wings and coiling mouthparts_____ .

5. Other insects in this order include the tiger moth, _____cecropia moth_____, and _____skipper butterfly_____ .

Unit IV Reading

- The following multiple-choice questions are from the reading questions in the lessons of Unit IV. Circle your answer.

1. What does a moth spin around itself? **(cloth, string, (silk))**

2. A moth's antennae, or feelers, are: **(thin, (feathery,) round)**

3. A butterfly's antennae are: **(pointed, feathery, (round))**

4. On its body, a butterfly has a coat of: **(silk, (hairs,) feathers)**

5. A monarch butterfly is colored: **(orange, black, (both))**

58

Observation and Sketching

- Review the insects from Order Lepidoptera. How are they alike?
- Contrast them and find their differences.
- Analyze the parts of the insects and label them. Draw two below.

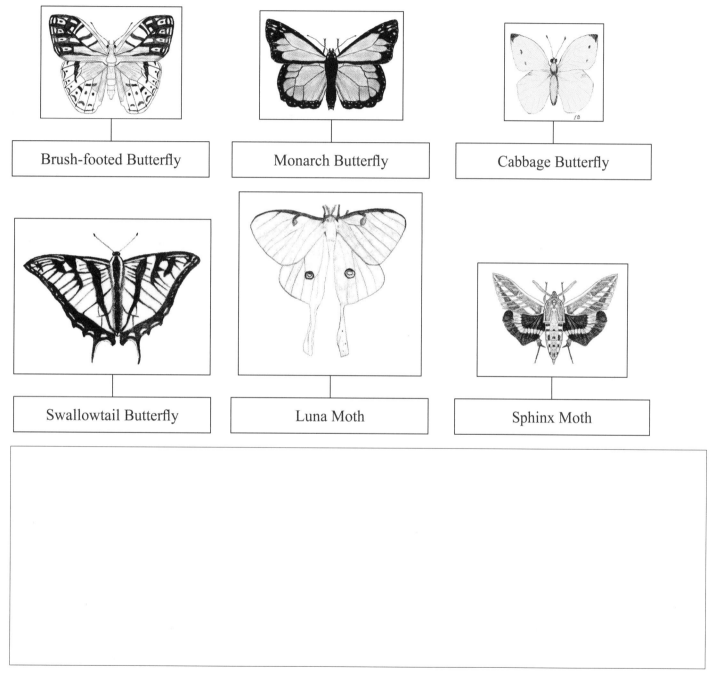

Brush-footed Butterfly

Monarch Butterfly

Cabbage Butterfly

Swallowtail Butterfly

Luna Moth

Sphinx Moth

Activities

1. Recite from memory the **Facts** you have learned about Orders Odonata, Orthoptera, Dictyoptera, Diptera, Coleoptera, and Lepidoptera (Moths & Butterflies).
2. Study your flashcards and all of Unit IV. Reread lessons in the textbook.

UNIT V
Hymenoptera

Lesson 24: Wasps

Order Facts

- Hymenoptera [Greek: υμεν + πτερα] means "membrane-winged"
- Paper wasp, yellow jacket, hornet, carpenter ant, fire ant, honeybee, bumblebee
- Complete metamorphosis
- Characteristics: slender waist and stingers
- Also includes: saw fly, mud dauber, bulldog ant, sweat bee

Reading and Questions

Insects Reader pp. 139-142

1. Why might a wasp sting you? It might sting if you press it, flap at it, or dodge it.

2. Where does the queen wasp spend the winter? She has stayed under the moss or grass.

3. What does the wasp use to make cells for its eggs and grubs? It uses fiber from plants and trees or shreds of wood from a window or post.

4. What do the grubs do once they become adult wasps? They work to help build the nest and feed other grubs, so that the queen can just lay eggs.

5. What are four specific kinds of wasps? There is the hornet, wall wasp, common wasp, wood wasp, and sand wasp.

6. When comparing the shapes of different kinds of wasps, what should you particularly notice? Notice the difference in the thread joining the thorax and abdomen.

Observation and Sketching

- Compare the body shape, antennae, and wings of the paper wasp, hornet, and yellow jacket. How are they alike?

- Contrast them and find their differences. Look especially at the markings on their abdomen.

- Analyze the parts of the hornet, and then draw your own version of it in the space below.

Paper Wasp

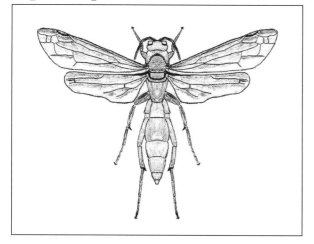

Hornet

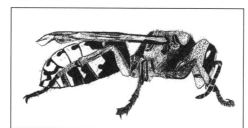

Yellow Jacket

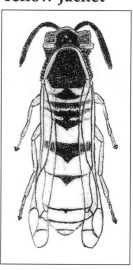

Activities

1. Recite from memory the **Facts** you have learned about Orders Odonata, Orthoptera, Dictyoptera, Diptera, Coleoptera, Lepidoptera, and Hymenoptera.

2. Find an old paper wasps' nest and draw a picture of it.

Lesson 25: Ants I

Order Facts

- Hymenoptera [Greek: υμεν + πτερα] means "membrane-winged"
- Paper wasp, yellow jacket, hornet, carpenter ant, fire ant, honeybee, bumblebee
- Complete metamorphosis
- Characteristics: slender waist and stingers
- Also includes: saw fly, mud dauber, bulldog ant, sweat bee

Reading and Questions

Insects Reader pp. 143-147

1. What insects belong to the "hook-wing family"? Ants, bees, saw flies, and wasps are in the hook-wing family.

2. What are the jaws of hook-wing insects used for? The jaws are used for cutting and carrying things.

3. Why is the sting of some hook-wing insects like a sword? The sting is used to fight with or to kill things for food.

4. What parts of the ant seem like they would be heavy to carry? The head and eyes seem heavy to carry.

5. What are the three kinds of ants in an ant hill? The ants are the workers, drones, and queen.

6. Why is "mother ant" a better name than "queen ant"? The queen ant does not rule. She makes eggs, works, and defends the colony.

7. What does an ant larva look like? It looks like a small white worm.

8. What is the white case that some people think are ant eggs? It is a pupa case.

Observation and Sketching

- Compare the paper wasp and carpenter ant. How are their bodies shaped alike?
- Contrast their bodies (e.g., legs) and find their differences.
- Analyze the parts of the carpenter ant, and then draw your own version of it in the space below.

Paper Wasp

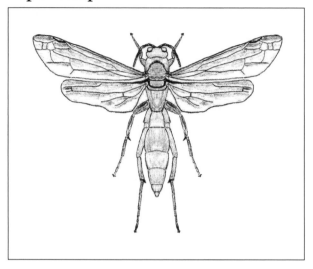

Carpenter Ant

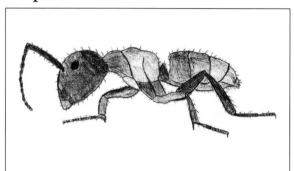

Activities

1. Read pp. 147-149, "The Ant's Home," in the *Insects Reader* and answer the following question: Does an ant hill have dining rooms? ___Yes, along with pantries, bedrooms, and nurseries.___

2. Recite from memory the **Facts** you have learned about Orders Odonata, Orthoptera, Dictyoptera, Diptera, Coleoptera, Lepidoptera, and Hymenoptera.

Lesson 26: Ants II

Order Facts

- Hymenoptera [Greek: υμεν + πτερα] means "membrane-winged"
- Paper wasp, yellow jacket, hornet, carpenter ant, fire ant, honeybee, bumblebee
- Complete metamorphosis
- Characteristics: slender waist and stingers
- Also includes: saw fly, mud dauber, bulldog ant, sweat bee

Reading and Questions

Insects Reader pp. 149-153

1. What will the worker ant do to make the queen stay in the hill? The worker will take off her wings if she tries to fly, and he will carry her back in his jaws if she tries to walk away.

2. What do ants do when they are "torpid" in the winter? They sleep.

3. What kinds of food do ants like to eat? They like honey, sugar, and seeds.

4. What is the name for the way ants sometimes cling together in a ball for safety or warmth? It is called snugging.

5. What does the brown mason ant use to build its nest? It uses little balls of mud like bricks.

6. Which ant bores into trees or logs to make its nest? It is the carpenter ant.

7. Why might ants go to war? They may war to get slaves or cows. They may also fight to protect their hill.

Observation and Sketching

- Compare the carpenter ant and fire ant. How are they alike?
- Contrast them and find their differences. Contrast how many knobs each has between the thorax and abdomen.
- Analyze the parts of the fire ant, and then draw your own version of it in the space below.

Carpenter Ant

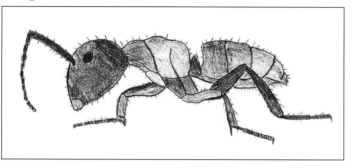

Fire Ant

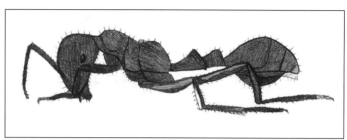

Activities

1. Read pp. 154-157, "Ants and Their Honey Cows," in the *Insects Reader*, and answer the following question: How many knobs does a red ant have? <u>It has two knobs.</u>
2. Recite from memory the **Facts** you have learned about Orders Odonata, Orthoptera, Dictyoptera, Diptera, Coleoptera, Lepidoptera, and Hymenoptera.

Lesson 27: Bees I

Order Facts

- Hymenoptera [Greek: υμεν + πτερα] means "membrane-winged"
- Paper wasp, yellow jacket, hornet, carpenter ant, fire ant, honeybee, bumblebee
- Complete metamorphosis
- Characteristics: slender waist and stingers
- Also includes: saw fly, mud dauber, bulldog ant, sweat bee

Reading and Questions

Insects Reader pp. 158-162

1. How many bees may live in a hive? <u>There may be twenty thousand to sixty thousand bees in a hive.</u>

2. How many queens rule over a bee hive? <u>One queen rules the hive.</u>

3. If bees were left to themselves, where would they find a home? <u>Bees may find a home in a hollow tree, under a house's roof, or in some other cavity (i.e., hollow place).</u>

4. Which bee wanders aimlessly about the hive and waits for the others to feed him and house him? <u>It is the drone bee.</u>

5. What does a worker bee hold in pockets under its abdomen? <u>It holds wax.</u>

Observation and Sketching

- Compare the honeybee and bumblebee bodies. How are they alike?
- Contrast them and find their differences.
- Analyze the parts of the honeybee, and then draw your own version of it in the space below.

Honeybee

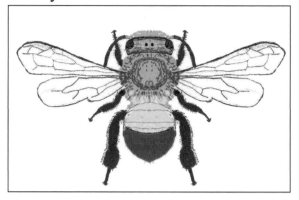

Bumblebee

Activities

1. Recite from memory the **Facts** you have learned about Orders Odonata, Orthoptera, Dictyoptera, Diptera, Coleoptera, Lepidoptera, and Hymenoptera.
2. Make new flashcards and study old ones.

Lesson 28: Bees II

Order Facts

- Hymenoptera [Greek: υμεν + πτερα] means "membrane-winged"
- Paper wasp, yellow jacket, hornet, carpenter ant, fire ant, honeybee, bumblebee
- Complete metamorphosis
- Characteristics: slender waist and stingers
- Also includes: saw fly, mud dauber, bulldog ant, sweat bee

Reading and Questions

Insects Reader pp. 162-167

1. How deep are the tubes made by the nursing bees, and how many sides do they have? _____
   The tubes are a half-inch deep and they have six sides.

2. What two kinds of things will be put into these cells? __Honey or bee eggs will be put into the cells.__

3. Do the honeybees waste space when making their hive? _____
   No, they use the least amount of wax and are able to fill "every atom of space."

4. Name two kinds of bees that do not live in hives, and tell where they live.
   The upholster bee digs a hole in the ground, and the mason bee builds a round hole in a wall.

5. What is the little hairy groove on a honeybee's leg that is used to carry pollen called? _____
   It is the bee's "basket."

6. When the queen bee goes flying outside the hive, does she go alone? __No, a group of drones flies__ with her as an "honor guard."

7. What kind of eggs does the queen bee lay after laying drone eggs? _____
   She lays "princess" or "queen" eggs.

Observation and Sketching

- Compare the worker, drone, and queen honeybee. How are they alike?
- Contrast them and find their differences.
- Analyze the parts of the worker bee, and then draw your own version of it in the space below.

Worker Bee

Queen Bee

Drone Bee

Activities

1. Read pp. 172-175, "Hive Bees," in the *Insects Reader*, and answer the following question: On one trip to flowers, does a honeybee visit different kinds of flowers? _____No_____
2. Recite from memory the **Facts** you have learned about Orders Odonata, Orthoptera, Dictyoptera, Diptera, Coleoptera, Lepidoptera, and Hymenoptera.

Lesson 29: Bees III

Order Facts

- Hymenoptera [Greek: υμεν + πτερα] means "membrane-winged"
- Paper wasp, yellow jacket, hornet, carpenter ant, fire ant, honeybee, bumblebee
- Complete metamorphosis
- Characteristics: slender waist and stingers
- Also includes: saw fly, mud dauber, bulldog ant, sweat bee

Reading and Questions

Insects Reader pp. 167-172

1. What happens to the old queen once a new "princess" bee is ready to take over? __The old__ queen swarms with some of the bees and goes to build a new hive.

2. How is the princess kept away from the old queen? __Worker bees close the hole over the__ princess's cell with food inside until the old queen has gone.

3. What happens if two princesses are born on the same day? __They will eventually meet and__ fight. The one who kills the other becomes the new queen.

4. If no new swarm wishes to start, what will the new queen do to all the other royal cells? She will open the cells one by one to sting and kill all the young princesses.

5. Give two reasons why the worker bees kill the drones after their last flight with the queen before winter. __The drones would die of starvation anyway, and since their work is done, they would__ be useless mouths to feed.

6. When the bees want to "ventilate" the hive because of heat and impure air, what do they use as a fan? __They use their wings.__

7. Name three kinds of "thieves and vagabonds" that may invade the hive. __e.g., wasps, snails,__ slugs, wax moths

Observation and Sketching

- Analyze the scenes below. What is being pictured in each scene?
- Draw your own version of the queen laying eggs.

Bee Hive

Queen Laying Eggs

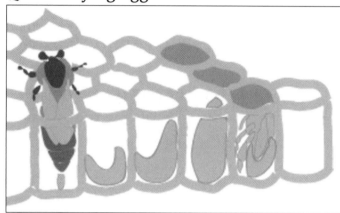

Activities

1. Read pp. 176-178, "Solitary Bees," in the *Insects Reader* and answer the following question: Do solitary bees store up honey in the winter? ___No.___

2. Recite from memory the **Facts** you have learned about Orders Odonata, Orthoptera, Dictyoptera, Diptera, Coleoptera, Lepidoptera, and Hymenoptera.

Lesson 30: Helpful & Harmful Insects

Order Facts

Helpful Insects
- Pollinate plants
- Control pests
- Make goods
- Decompose dead things

Harmful Insects
- Destroy plants
- Damage goods
- Spread disease

Reading and Questions

Insects Reader pp. 179-183

1. What is pollination? What does it do? ___Pollination is the way pollen is moved from one plant to another. It fertilizes plants so they can bear fruit and multiply.___

2. Give four examples of insects that pollinate plants. ___e.g., bees, wasps, ants, beetles, moths and butterflies, flies___

3. What do the termite, sexton beetle, and dung beetle have in common? ___They were made especially to help tidy and clean up the world.___

4. What insect does harm to plants and makes a juice called honeydew? ___aphids___

5. What does the mosquito carry inside it that can cause disease? ___parasites and viruses___

6. What are two deadly diseases carried by mosquitoes? ___dengue fever and yellow fever___

7. What is the best natural controller of mosquitoes? ___dragonflies___

8. What are some uses of honey? ___e.g., spread on food, sweetener, medicine___

9. At what stage do moths produce silk? ___pupa___

Observation and Sketching

- Identify the insects below as "helpful," harmful," or "both."
- Find a drawing or photograph that shows either the benefit(s) of a helpful insect or the damage and harm of a harmful insect. Sketch your own version of it in the space below.

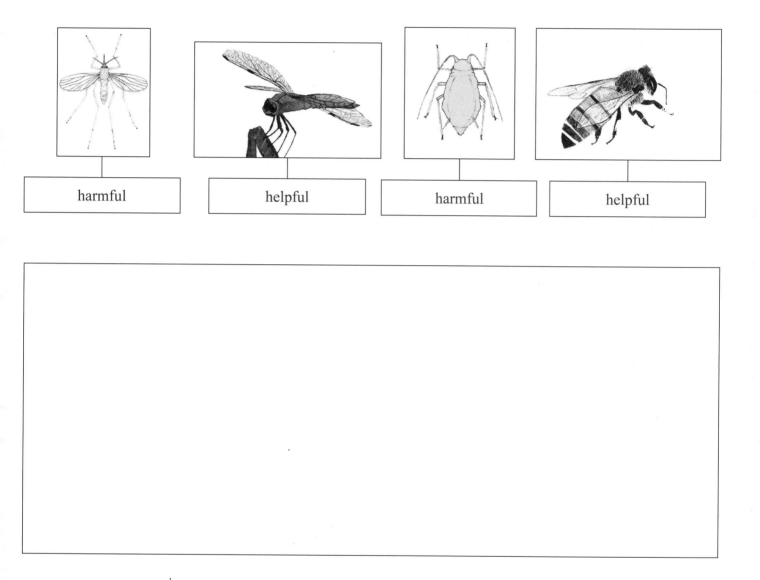

harmful	helpful	harmful	helpful

Activities

1. Recite from memory the **Facts** you have learned about Orders Odonata, Orthoptera, Dictyoptera, Diptera, Coleoptera, Lepidoptera, Hymenoptera, and Helpful and Harmful Insects.
2. Study your flashcards and all of Unit V. Review lessons in the textbook.

Lesson 31: Unit V Review

Unit V Facts

Hymenoptera Facts

1. Order Hymenoptera means "_____membrane_____ - winged."
2. This order includes insects like the paper wasp, yellow _____jacket_____,
   hornet, carpenter ___ant___, fire ant, honeybee, and _____bumblebee_____.
3. Insects in this order grow by _____complete_____ metamorphosis.
4. Insects in this order are characterized by a _____slender waist_____
   and _____stingers_____.
5. Other insects in this order include the saw fly, _____mud_____ dauber,
   _____bulldog_____ ant, and sweat bee.

Helpful and Harmful Insects Facts

1. Helpful insects _____pollinate_____ plants, decompose ___dead___ things, control
   _____pests_____, and make goods.
2. Harmful insects _____destroy_____ plants, spread _____disease_____, and damage
   _____goods_____.

Unit V Reading

1. The sting of some hook-wing insects is like a _____sword_____.
2. The _____drone_____ bee wanders aimlessly about the hive and waits for
   the others to feed him and house him.
3. The little hairy groove on a honeybee's leg that is used to carry pollen is called the
   _____basket_____.
4. If a new "princess" bee is ready to take over, the old queen _____swarms_____.
5. _____Pollination_____ is the way pollen is moved from one plant to another.
6. Mosquitoes can carry _____dengue_____ fever and yellow fever.
7. The best natural controller of mosquitoes is the _____dragonfly_____.

Observation and Sketching

- Review the insects from Order Hymenoptera. How are they alike?
- Contrast them and find their differences.
- Analyze the parts of the insects and label them. Draw two below.

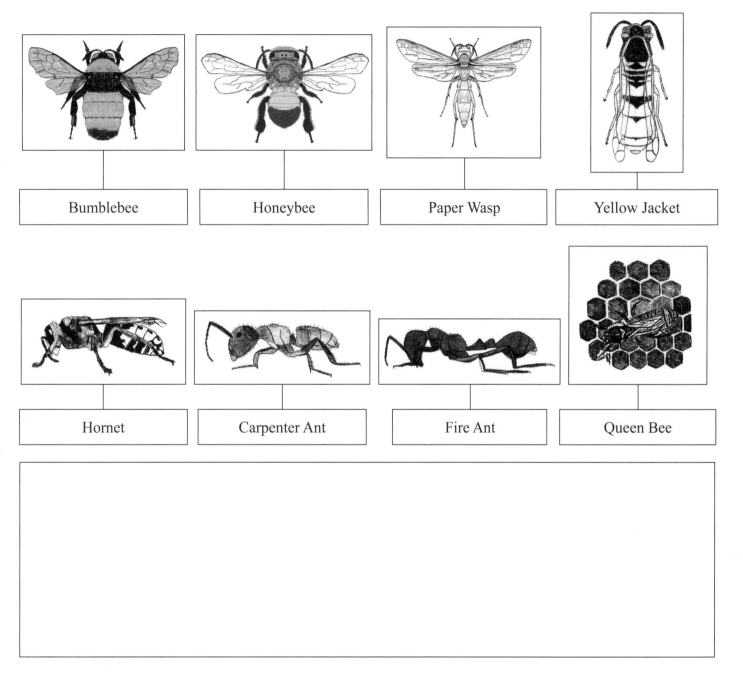

| Bumblebee | Honeybee | Paper Wasp | Yellow Jacket |

| Hornet | Carpenter Ant | Fire Ant | Queen Bee |

Activities

1. Recite from memory the **Facts** you have learned about Orders Odonata, Orthoptera, Dictyoptera, Diptera, Coleoptera, Lepidoptera, and Hymenoptera.
2. Study your flashcards and all of Unit V. Reread lessons in the textbook.

Lesson 32: Final Review

Order Facts

Odonata Facts

1. Odonata means "_____toothed_____."
2. What two kinds of insects are in Order Odonata? _____dragonflies and damselflies_____
   _____
3. Insects in Odonata grow by _____incomplete_____ metamorphosis.
4. The characteristics of Order Odonata are _____water nymphs and needle-like abdomen_____
   _____ .

Orthoptera Facts

1. Orthoptera means "_____straight-winged_____."
2. Order Orthoptera includes grasshoppers, crickets, _____mantids and cockroaches_____
   _____ .
3. Insects in Orthoptera grow by _____incomplete_____ metamorphosis.
4. The characteristics of Order Orthoptera are _____fan-like hind wings and leathery front wings_____
   _____ .
5. Other insects in this order include katydids, locusts, and _____walking stick_____ .

Dictyoptera Facts

6. Dictyoptera means "_____net-winged_____."
7. Order Dictyoptera includes cockroaches and _____mantids_____
8. Insects in Dictyoptera grow by _____incomplete_____ metamorphosis.
9. The characteristics of Order Dictyoptera are _____fan-like hind wings and leathery front wings_____
   _____ .

Hemiptera Facts

1. Hemiptera means "_____half-winged_____."
2. Order Hemiptera includes water bugs and _____hoppers_____ .
3. Insects in Hemiptera grow by _____incomplete_____ metamorphosis.
4. The characteristics of Order Hemiptera are _____first half of wing is rough, but the tip is
   smooth_____
5. Other insects in this order include cicadas, aphids, and other _____true bugs_____

Diptera Facts

1. Diptera means "_____two-winged_____."
2. Order Diptera includes the house fly, crane fly, horse fly, mosquito and _____bluebottle_____.
3. Insects in Diptera grow by _____complete_____ metamorphosis.
4. The characteristics of Order Diptera are_____soft body and sucking mouthparts_____.
5. Other insects in this order include the gnat, midge, fruit-fly, and _____bot-fly_____.

Coleoptera Facts

1. Coleoptera means "_____sheath-winged_____."
2. Order Coleoptera includes the ladybug, firefly, ground beetle, _____whirligig beetle, Japanese beetle, and sweet potato weevil_____
_____
3. Insects in Coleoptera grow by _____complete_____ metamorphosis.
4. The characteristics of Order Coleoptera are_____front wings are hard and meet down the middle of the back_____
5. Other insects in this order include the click beetle, june bug, cocktail, tiger beetle, and _____stag beetle_____.

Lepidoptera Facts

1. Lepidoptera means "_____scale-winged_____."
2. Insects in Lepidoptera grow by _____complete_____ metamorphosis.
3. The characteristics of Order Lepidoptera are_____large wings and coiling mouthparts_____
_____.
4. Other insects in this order include the tiger moth, _____cecropia moth_____, and _____skipper butterfly_____.

Hymenoptera Facts

1. Order Hymenoptera means "_____membrane_____-winged."
2. This order includes insects like the paper wasp, yellow _____jacket_____, hornet, carpenter _____ant_____, fire ant, honeybee, and _____bumblebee_____.
3. Insects in this order grow by _____complete_____ metamorphosis.
4. Insects in this order are characterized by a _____slender waist_____ and _____stingers_____.
5. Other insects in this order include the saw fly, _____mud_____ dauber, _____bulldog_____ ant, and sweat bee.

Observation and Sketching

- First, fill in the missing order names and the names of all the insects.
- Then review the insects from all the orders of insects. How are they **all** alike? How are the insects within each order alike?
- Now contrast the orders and find their **main** differences. Also, contrast the insects within each order.
- Lastly, analyze the parts of the insects, and label them.

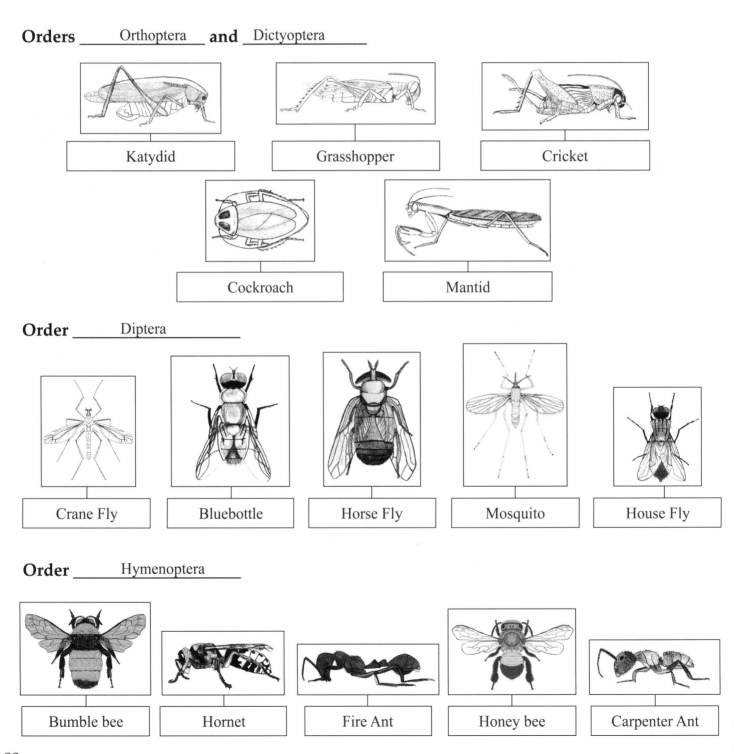

Orders _____ Orthoptera _____ **and** _____ Dictyoptera _____

Katydid

Grasshopper

Cricket

Cockroach

Mantid

Order _____ Diptera _____

Crane Fly

Bluebottle

Horse Fly

Mosquito

House Fly

Order _____ Hymenoptera _____

Bumble bee

Hornet

Fire Ant

Honey bee

Carpenter Ant

Order _____Lepidoptera_____

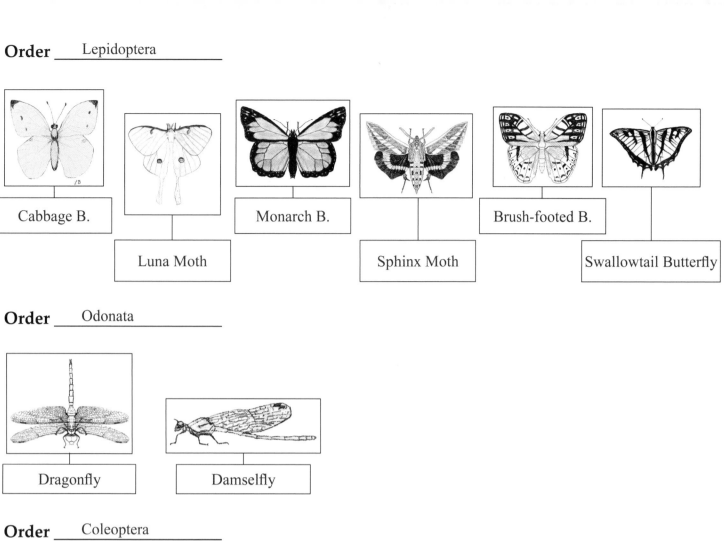

Cabbage B.

Luna Moth

Monarch B.

Sphinx Moth

Brush-footed B.

Swallowtail Butterfly

Order _____Odonata_____

Dragonfly

Damselfly

Order _____Coleoptera_____

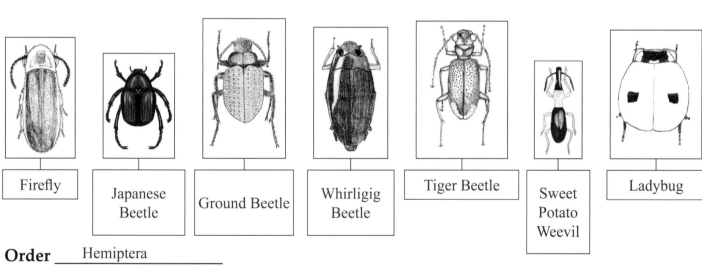

Firefly

Japanese Beetle

Ground Beetle

Whirligig Beetle

Tiger Beetle

Sweet Potato Weevil

Ladybug

Order _____Hemiptera_____

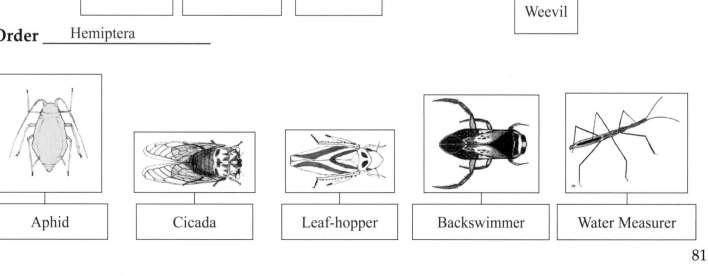

Aphid

Cicada

Leaf-hopper

Backswimmer

Water Measurer

Insect Flashcards

These can be copied and pasted on cardstock paper to serve as quick review with students.

Order Odonata

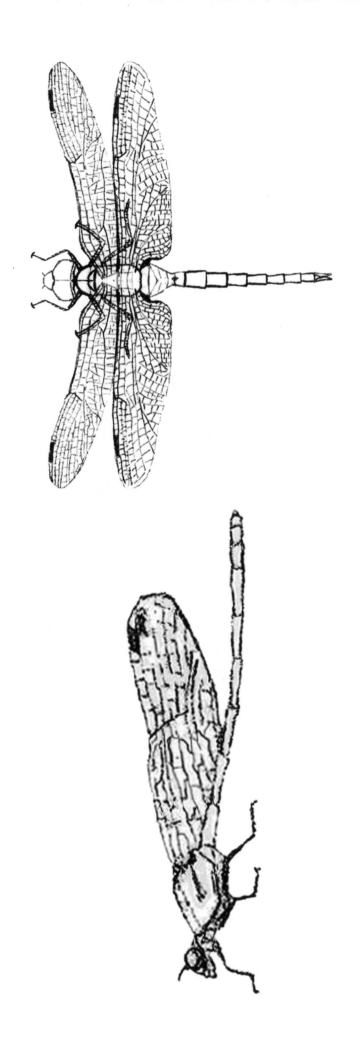

Order Orthoptera and Dictyoptera

Order Hemiptera

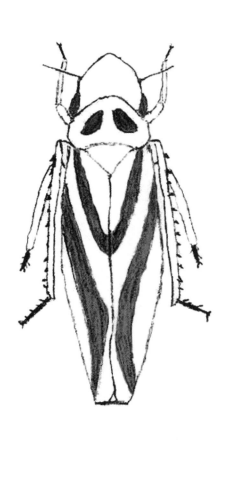

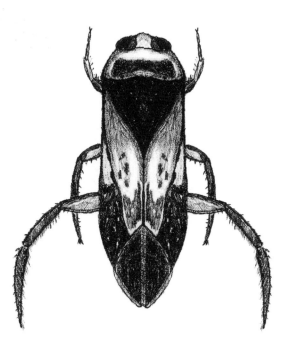

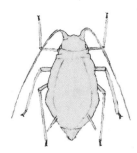

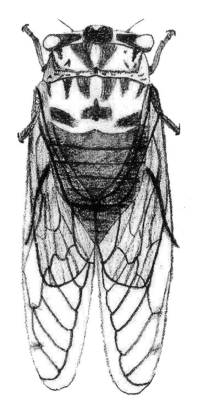

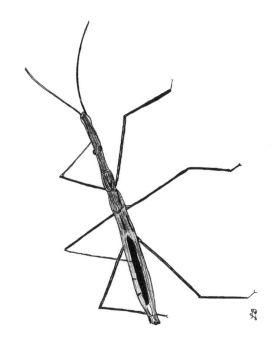

Order Diptera

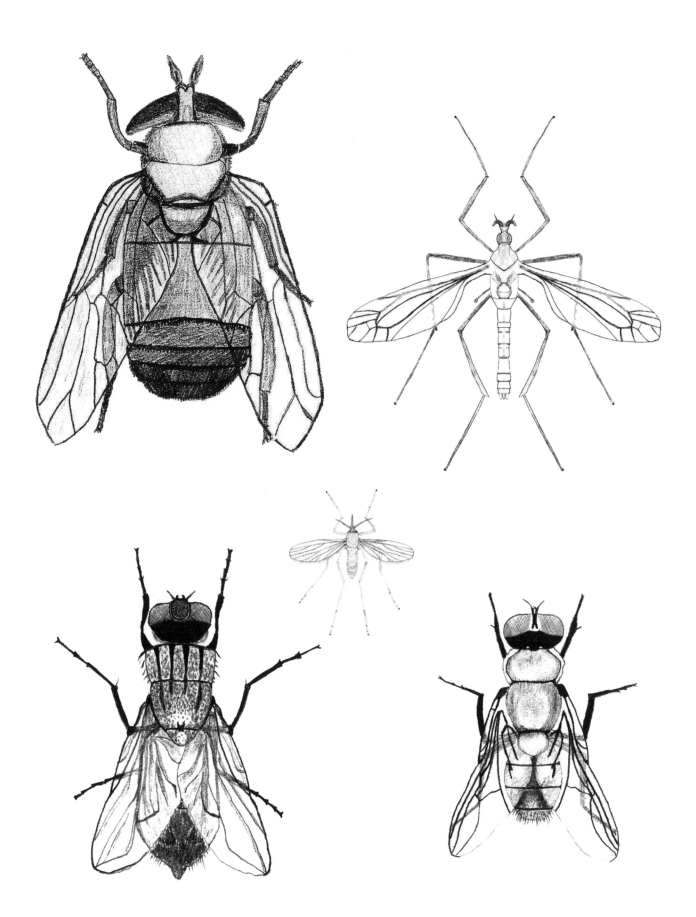

Order Coleoptera

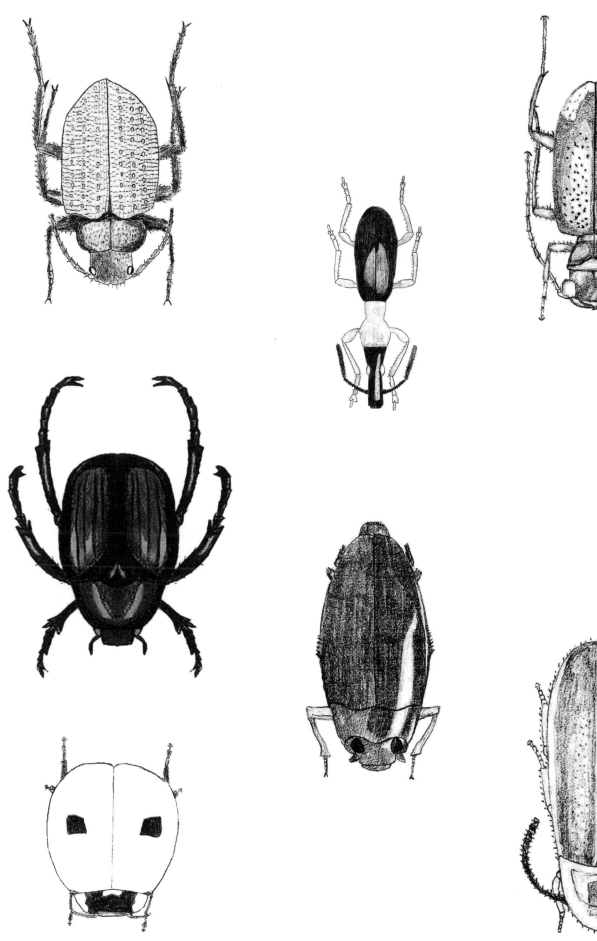

Order Lepidoptera

Order Hymenoptera

Blank Quizzes and Tests

Lesson 1 Quiz: *What Is an Insect?*

Name: _____ Date: _____

I. Label the parts of the insect using the words from the word bank.

abdomen	antennae	eye	foreleg	forewing
hindleg	ovipositor	spiracles	thorax	head

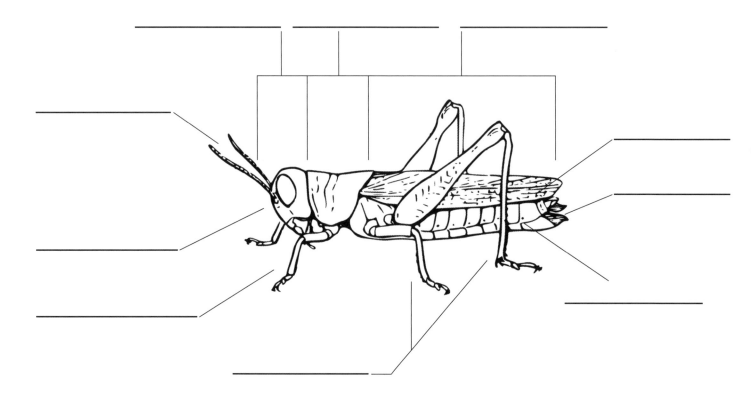

II. Short Answer

1. How many legs do insects have? _____

2. How many wings do insects have? _____

3. How many main body parts does an insect have? _____

4. How does an insect breathe air? _____

5. From the tail of the insect to its head, it is divided into what? _____

Lesson 2 Quiz: *Insects and Other Animals*

Name: _____   Date: _____

I. Draw a circle around the insects only.

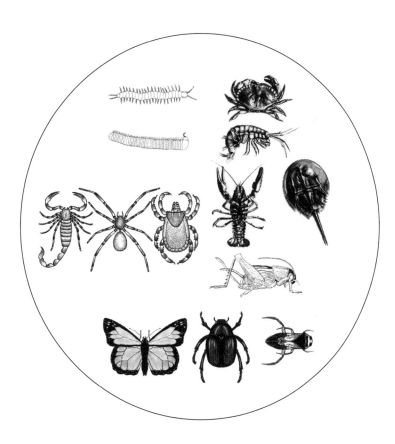

II. Short Answer

1. What group of similar animals do insects belong in? _____

2. Arthropods have an exoskeleton, segmented body, and what kind of legs?

   _____

3. Arthropod classes are separated by what?_____

   _____

4. How many legs do arachnids have? _____

5. How many legs do crustaceans have?_____

6. How many legs do insects have? _____

Lesson 3 Quiz: *Different Orders of Insects*

Name: _____   Date: _____

I. Label the missing Orders using names from the word bank. The first is done for you.

Diptera	*Coleoptera*	*Lepidoptera*	*Dictyoptera*
Orthoptera	*Hemiptera*	*Hymenoptera*	

Odonata

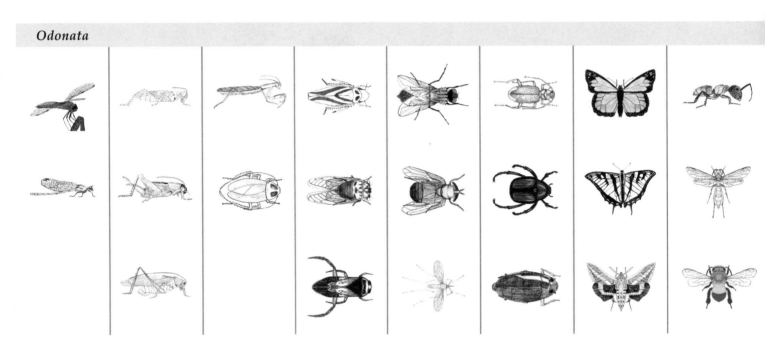

II. Short Answer

1. What is the class called insects divided into? _____

    _____

2. The Orders are defined by the shape of what? _____

    _____

3. What are the Eight Orders in this book? _____

    _____

    _____

    _____

4. Name one insect from Order Odonata._____

5. Name one insect from Order Lepidoptera._____

Lesson 4 Quiz: *What Is Metamorphosis?*

Name: _____   Date: _____

I. Label the kinds of metamorphosis and their stages using the words from the word bank.

Incomplete	Complete	Egg (2)	Adult (2)
Nymph	Pupa	Larva	

_____ metamorphosis

_____ metamorphosis

II. Short Answer

1. What do we call the way insects grow? _____

2. What are the two kinds of metamorphosis? _____

   _____

3. What are the stages of incomplete metamorphosis? _____

   _____

4. What are the stages of complete metamorphosis? _____

   _____

Unit I Test

Name: _____   Date: _____

I. Label the boxes with the missing names (14 total).

Complete Metamorphosis

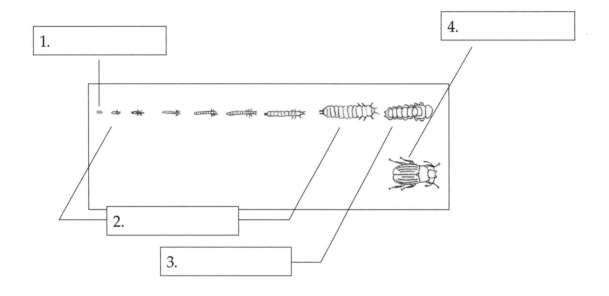

5.	Orthoptera & Dictyoptera	6.		Diptera	7.		Lepidoptera	Hymenoptera

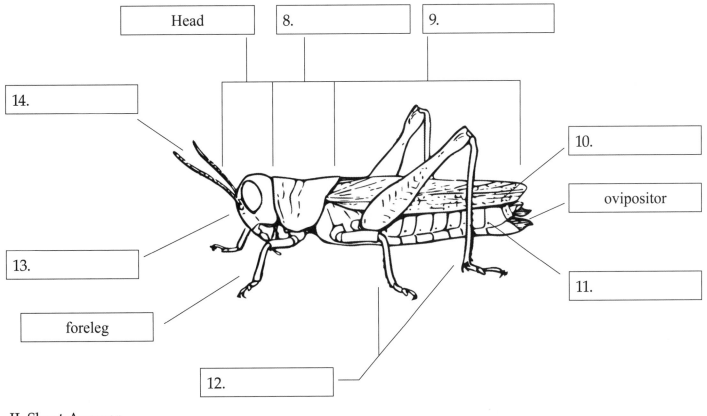

Head   8.   9.

14.

10.

ovipositor

13.

11.

foreleg

12.

II. Short Answer

1. Insects are animals with a body made of _____ .

2. How many legs do all insects have? _____

3. Insects belong with other similar animals in a group called _____ .

4. What three characteristics do all Arthropods have?_____

_____

_____

5. Metamorphosis is how insects _____ .

6. What are the stages of incomplete metamorphosis? _____

_____

7. What are the stages of complete metamorphosis?_____

_____

8. The class called "Insects" is divided into _____ .

9. How much of the animal kingdom is made up of insects? _____

10. Arthropods are divided into Classes based on their _____ .

11. How many legs do Arachnids have? _____

Lessons 6-7 Quiz: Odonata

Name: _____   Date: _____

I. Identify the main insects of this order by writing the name of each insect under its picture.

II. Fill in the meaning for the Order name.

Order	English meaning
Odonata	

III. Short Answer

1. Insects in this order have _____ metamorphosis.

2. What are the two main characteristics you learned for this order?

   a. _____

   b. _____

3. Why are dragonflies not easy to catch? _____

   _____

4. Where may dragonflies be found? _____

Lessons 8-9 Quiz: Orthoptera and Dictyoptera

Name: _____   Date: _____

I. Identify the main insects of these orders by writing the name of each insect under its picture.

II. Fill in the meaning for the Order name.

Order	English meaning	Order	English meaning
Orthoptera		Dictyoptera	

III. Short Answer

1. Insects in these orders have _____ metamorphosis.

2. What are the two main characteristics you learned for these orders?

   a. _____

   b. _____

3. How do grasshoppers and crickets make their chirping sound? _____

   _____

4. I eat everything I can get, including people's food, and some people say I smell bad. Who am I? _____

Lessons 10-11 Quiz: Hemiptera

Name: _____   Date: _____

I. Identify the main insects of this order by writing the name of each insect under its picture.

II. Fill in the meaning for the Order name.

Order	English meaning
Hemiptera	

III. Short Answer

1. Insects in this order have _____ metamorphosis.

2. What are the two main characteristics you learned for this order?

   a. _____

   b. _____

3. What does the water measurer have under his body and on his legs that keeps him from getting wet and sinking? _____

4. What is called "the singer," "the screamer," and "the squealer"? _____

Unit II Test

Name: _____   Date: _____

I. Identify the main insects of this unit by writing the name of each insect under its picture. Then circle the order to which it belongs.

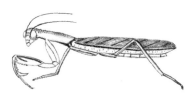

_____
A. Odonata
B. Dictyoptera

_____
A. Hemiptera
B. Odonata

_____
A. Hemiptera
B. Odonata

_____
A. Hemiptera
B. Dictyoptera

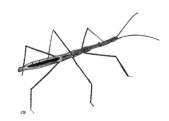

_____
A. Orthoptera
B. Odonata

_____
A. Orthoptera
B. Hemiptera

_____
A. Odonata
B. Orthoptera

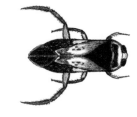

_____
A. Hemiptera
B. Odonata

_____
A. Orthoptera
B. Odonata

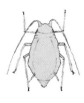

_____
A. Odonata
B. Hemiptera

_____
A. Hemiptera
B. Odonata

_____
A. Orthoptera
B. Odonata

II. Fill in the blank with either the meaning for the Order name or the Order.

Order	English meaning
Odonata	
	half-winged
Orthoptera	
	net-winged

III. Circle the answer that makes the statement true.

1. **(Odonata / Orthoptera / Hemiptera)** has fan-like hind wings.

2. **(Odonata / Orthoptera / Hemiptera)** has aquatic nymphs.

3. **(Odonata / Orthoptera / Hemiptera)** has smooth wing tips.

4. **(Odonata / Orthoptera / Hemiptera)** has rough first half of wing.

5. **(Odonata / Orthoptera / Hemiptera)** has needle-like abdomens.

6. **(Odonata / Orthoptera / Hemiptera)** has leathery front wings.

7. Odonata has **(complete / incomplete)** metamorphosis.

8. Hemiptera has **(complete / incomplete)** metamorphosis.

9. Dictyoptera has **(complete / incomplete)** metamorphosis.

Lessons 13-14 Quiz: Diptera

Name: _____ Date: _____

I. Identify the main insects of this order by writing the name of each insect under its picture.

II. Fill in the meaning for the Order name.

Order	English meaning
Diptera	

III. Short Answer

1. Insects in this order have _____ metamorphosis.

2. What are the two main characteristics you learned for this order?

    a. _____

    b. _____

3. What is the name of a fly larva? _____

4. What do the hairs and pad on a fly's foot act like? _____

    _____

Lessons 15-17 Quiz: Coleoptera

Name: _____   Date: _____

I. Identify the main insects of this order by writing the name of each insect under its picture.

II. Fill in the meaning for the Order name.

Order	English meaning
Coleoptera	

III. Short Answer

1. Insects in this order have _____ metamorphosis.

2. What are the two main characteristics you learned for this order?

    a. _____

    b. _____

3. Why is a ladybug a useful beetle? _____

4. What are the hard cases over the beetle's back? _____

Unit III Test

Name: _____   Date: _____

I. Identify the main insects of this unit by writing the name of each insect under its picture. Then circle the order to which it belongs.

_____
A. Diptera
B. Coleoptera

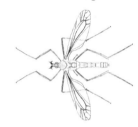

_____
A. Diptera
B. Coleoptera

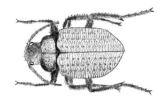

_____
A. Diptera
B. Coleoptera

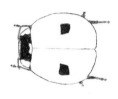

_____
A. Diptera
B. Coleoptera

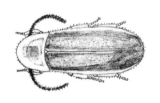

_____
A. Diptera
B. Coleoptera

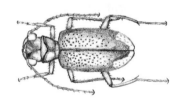

_____
A. Diptera
B. Coleoptera

_____
A. Diptera
B. Coleoptera

_____
A. Diptera
B. Coleoptera

_____
A. Diptera
B. Coleoptera

_____
A. Diptera
B. Coleoptera

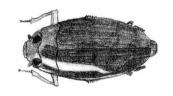

_____
A. Diptera
B. Coleoptera

_____
A. Diptera
B. Coleoptera

II. Fill in the blank with either the meaning for the Order name or the Order.

Order	English meaning
Coleoptera	
Diptera	

III. Circle the answer that makes the statement true.
1. **(Diptera / Coleoptera)** has soft bodies.
2. **(Diptera / Coleoptera)** has hard front wings.
3. **(Diptera / Coleoptera)** has front wings that meet down the middle of the back.
4. **(Diptera / Coleoptera)** has sucking mouth parts.
5. Diptera has **(complete / incomplete)** metamorphosis.
6. Coleoptera has **(complete / incomplete)** metamorphosis.

IV. Circle the best answer.
1. What is the name of a fly larva? **(maggot, worm, grub)**
2. Mrs. Fly lays her eggs in: **(water, hair, dead things)**
3. The hard cases over the beetle's back are: **(eggs, wings)**
4. This beetle is fast and fierce: **(tiger beetle, lady bug, firefly)**
5. This water beetle spins round and round: **(ground beetle, whirligig beetle, Japanese beetle)**

Lessons 19-20 Quiz: Moths

Name: _____   Date: _____

I. Identify the main insects of this order by writing the name of each insect under its picture.

II. Fill in the meaning for the Order name.

Order	English meaning
Lepidoptera	

III. Short Answer

1. Insects in this order have _____ metamorphosis.
2. What are the two main characteristics you learned for this order?
    a. _____
    b. _____
3. What is the difference between a moth's feelers and a butterfly's? _____

    _____

    _____

4. How does a moth hold its wings when it is not flying, or at rest? _____

    _____

    _____

Lessons 21-22 Quiz: Butterflies

Name: _____ Date: _____

I. Identify the main insects of this order by writing the name of each insect under its picture.

II. Fill in the meaning for the Order name.

Order	English meaning
Lepidoptera	

III. Short Answer

1. Insects in this order have _____ metamorphosis.

2. What are the two main characteristics you learned for this order?

   a. _____

   b. _____

3. When a caterpillar hatches, what does it eat? _____

   _____

4. Does a butterfly fly in a line or in a zig-zag? _____

Unit IV Test

Name: _____   Date: _____

I. Identify the main insects of this order by writing the name of each insect under its picture.

II. Fill in the meaning for the Order name.

Order	English meaning
Lepidoptera	

III. Circle the answer that makes the statement true.

1. Lepidoptera has **(complete / incomplete)** metamorphosis.
2. Order Lepidoptera includes the **(cauliflower / cabbage)** butterfly, sphinx moth, monarch butterfly, swallowtail butterfly, and brush-footed butterfly.
3. Other insects in this order include the tiger moth, **(cecropia / capillary)** moth, and skipper butterfly.

IV. Circle the best answer.

1. What does a moth spin around itself? **(string, silk, cloth)**

2. A moth's antennae, or feelers, are: **(round, feathery, thin)**

3. A butterfly's antennae are: **(feathery, pointed, round)**

4. On its body, a butterfly has a coat of: **(feathers, silk, hairs)**

5. A monarch butterfly is colored: **(black, orange, both)**

V. Short Answer

1. Insects in this order have _____ metamorphosis.

2. What are the two main characteristics you learned for this order?

   a. _____

   b. _____

Lessons 24-26 Quiz: Wasps and Ants

Name: _____   Date: _____

I. Identify the wasps and ants by writing the name of each insect under its picture.

[_____]   [_____]

[_____]   [_____]

II. Fill in the meaning for the Order name.

Order	English meaning
Hymenoptera	

III. Short Answer

1. Insects in this order have _____ metamorphosis.

2. What are the two main characteristics you learned for this order?

   a. _____

   b. _____

3. How many knobs does a red ant, or fire ant, have? _____

4. Why is the sting of some hook-wing insects like a sword? _____

   _____

5. When comparing the shapes of different kinds of wasps, what should you particularly notice?

   _____

Lessons 27-29 Quiz: Bees

Name: _____   Date: _____

I. Identify the bees by writing the name of each insect under its picture.

[ ]

[ ]

[ ]

[ ]

II. Fill in the meaning for the Order name.

Order	English meaning
Hymenoptera	

III. Short Answer

1. Insects in this order have _____ metamorphosis.

2. What are the two main characteristics you learned for this order?

   a. _____

   b. _____

3. How many queens rule over a bee hive? _____

4. Which bee wanders aimlessly about the hive and waits for the others to feed them and

   house them? _____

5. What is the little hairy groove on a honeybee's leg called? _____

   _____

6. What happens to the old queen once a new "princess" bee is ready to take over? _____

   _____

Unit V Test

Name: _____   Date: _____

I. Identify the main insects of this order by writing the name of each insect under its picture.

II. Fill in the meaning for the Order name.

Order	English meaning
Hymenoptera	

III. Circle the answer that makes the statement true.

1. Hymenoptera has **(complete / incomplete)** metamorphosis.
2. The sting of some hook-wing insects is like a **(needle / sword)**.
3. The little hairy groove on a honeybee's leg that is used to carry pollen is called the **(file / basket).**
4. **(Pollination / Polymorphosis)** is the way pollen is moved from one plant to another.
5. Mosquitoes can carry **(dengue / spotted)** fever and yellow fever.
6. The best natural controller of mosquitoes is the **(crane fly / dragonfly)**.

IV. Short Answer

1. This order includes insects like the paper wasp, yellow _____ ,
   hornet, carpenter _____ , fire ant, honeybee, and_____ .

2. Insects in this order are characterized by a _____
   and _____ .

3. Helpful insects _____ plants, decompose_____ things,
   control _____ and make goods.

4. Harmful insects _____ plants, spread _____, and damage
   _____.

5. Other insects in this order include the saw fly, _____dauber, _____
   ant, and sweat bee.

Final Test

Name: _____   Date: _____

I. Identify the insects of this study guide by writing the name of each insect under its picture. Then circle the order to which it belongs.

_____

A. Orthoptera
B. Coleoptera
C. Hemiptera

_____

A. Orthoptera
B. Coleoptera
C. Hemiptera

_____

A. Orthoptera
B. Coleoptera
C. Hemiptera

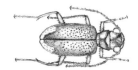

_____

A. Orthoptera
B. Coleoptera
C. Hemiptera

_____

A. Orthoptera
B. Coleoptera
C. Hemiptera

_____

A. Dictyoptera
B. Coleoptera
C. Hemiptera

_____

A. Orthoptera
B. Coleoptera
C. Hemiptera

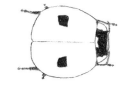

_____

A. Orthoptera
B. Coleoptera
C. Hemiptera

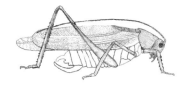

_____

A. Orthoptera
B. Coleoptera
C. Hemiptera

_____

A. Orthoptera
B. Coleoptera
C. Hemiptera

_____

A. Orthoptera
B. Coleoptera
C. Hemiptera

_____

A. Orthoptera
B. Coleoptera
C. Hemiptera

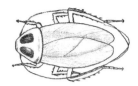

A. Dictyoptera B. Coleoptera C. Hemiptera	A. Orthoptera B. Coleoptera C. Hemiptera	A. Orthoptera B. Coleoptera C. Hemiptera

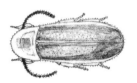

A. Orthoptera B. Coleoptera C. Hemiptera	A. Orthoptera B. Coleoptera C. Diptera	A. Odonata B. Lepidoptera C. Hymenoptera D. Diptera

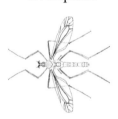

A. Odonata B. Lepidoptera C. Hymenoptera D. Diptera	A. Odonata B. Lepidoptera C. Hymenoptera D. Diptera	A. Odonata B. Lepidoptera C. Hymenoptera D. Diptera

A. Odonata B. Lepidoptera C. Hymenoptera D. Diptera	A. Odonata B. Lepidoptera C. Hymenoptera D. Diptera	A. Odonata B. Lepidoptera C. Hymenoptera D. Diptera

A. Odonata	A. Odonata	A. Odonata
B. Lepidoptera	B. Lepidoptera	B. Lepidoptera
C. Hymenoptera	C. Hymenoptera	C. Hymenoptera
D. Diptera	D. Diptera	D. Diptera

A. Odonata	A. Odonata	A. Odonata
B. Lepidoptera	B. Lepidoptera	B. Lepidoptera
C. Hymenoptera	C. Hymenoptera	C. Hymenoptera
D. Diptera	D. Diptera	D. Diptera

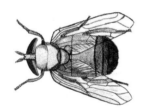

A. Odonata	A. Odonata	A. Odonata
B. Lepidoptera	B. Lepidoptera	B. Lepidoptera
C. Hymenoptera	C. Hymenoptera	C. Hymenoptera
D. Diptera	D. Diptera	D. Diptera

II. Give the English meaning for the Order names.

Order	English meaning
Coleoptera	
Diptera	
Hemiptera	
Hymenoptera	
Lepidoptera	
Odonata	
Dictyoptera	
Orthoptera	

III. Tell whether the insects in the orders grow by incomplete or complete metamorphosis. Circle Incomplete or Complete.

1. Coleoptera   **Incomplete**   **Complete**

2. Diptera   **Incomplete**   **Complete**

3. Hemiptera   **Incomplete**   **Complete**

4. Hymenoptera   **Incomplete**   **Complete**

5. Lepidoptera   **Incomplete**   **Complete**

6. Odonata   **Incomplete**   **Complete**

7. Orthoptera   **Incomplete**   **Complete**

8. Dictyoptera   **Incomplete**   **Complete**

IV. Give the characteristics for each order.

1. Coleoptera _____

_____

_____

2. Diptera _____

_____

_____

3. Hemiptera _____

_____

_____

4. Hymenoptera _____

_____

_____

5. Lepidoptera _____

_____

_____

6. Odonata _____

_____

_____

7. Orthoptera and Dictyoptera _____

_____

_____

Quiz and Test
Keys

Lesson 1 Quiz: *What Is an Insect?*

Name: _____   Date: _____

I. Label the parts of the insect using the words from the word bank.

abdomen	antennae	eye	foreleg	forewing
hindleg	ovipositor	spiracles	thorax	head

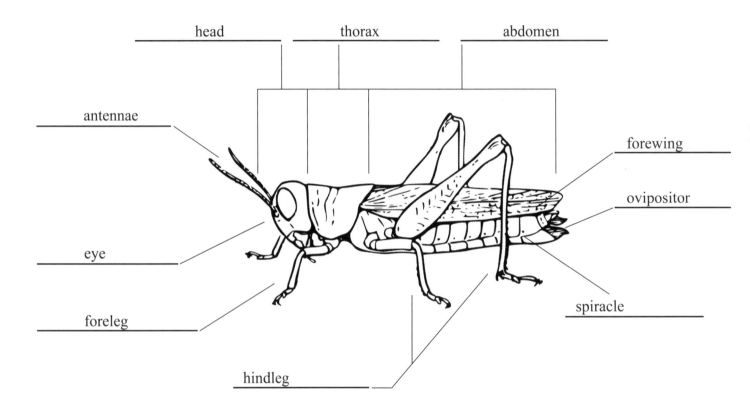

head   thorax   abdomen

antennae

forewing

ovipositor

eye

spiracle

foreleg

hindleg

II. Short Answer

1. How many legs do insects have? _____6_____
2. How many wings do insects have? __2 or 4_____
3. How many main body parts does an insect have? __3_____
4. How does an insect breathe air? ____spiracles_____
5. From the tail of the insect to its head, it is divided into what? __rings_____

Lesson 2 Quiz: *Insects and Other Animals*

Name: _____   Date: _____

I. Draw a circle around the insects only.

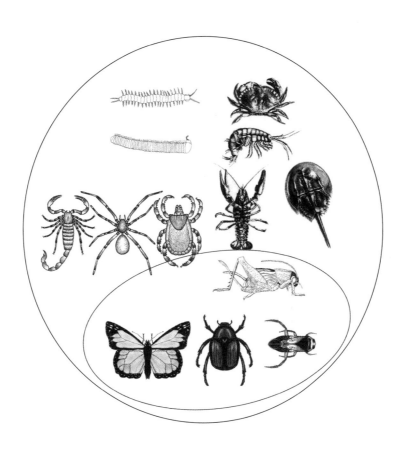

II. Short Answer

1. What group of similar animals do insects belong in? __Arthropods_____

2. Arthropods have an exoskeleton, segmented body, and what kind of legs? _____
   __jointed_____

3. Arthropod classes are separated by what?____how many legs they have_____
   _____

4. How many legs do Arachnids have? ____8_____

5. How many legs do Crustaceans have? ___10_____

6. How many legs do Insects have? _____6_____

Lesson 3 Quiz: *Different Orders of Insects*

Name: _____ Date: _____

I. Label the missing Orders using names from the word bank. The first is done for you.

Diptera	Coleoptera	Lepidoptera	Dictyoptera
Orthoptera	Hemiptera	Hymenoptera	

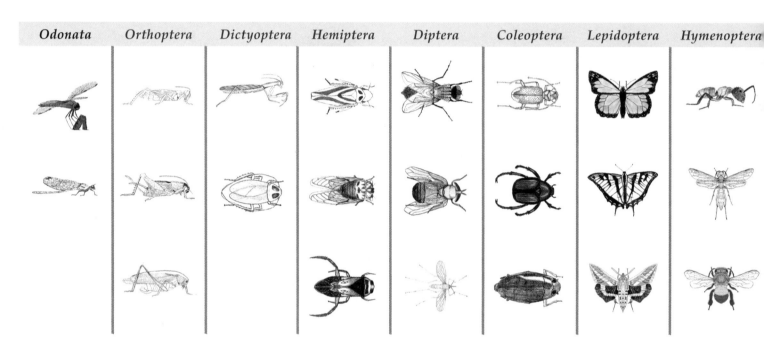

Odonata	Orthoptera	Dictyoptera	Hemiptera	Diptera	Coleoptera	Lepidoptera	Hymenoptera

II. Short Answer

1. What is the class called Insects divided into? _____Orders_____

2. The Orders are defined by the shape of what? _____their body_____

3. What are the eight Orders in this book? _____Odonata, Orthoptera, Dictyoptera, Hemiptera, Diptera, Coleoptera, Lepidoptera, Hymenoptera_____

4. Name one insect from Order Odonata. _____e.g., dragonfly, damselfly_____

5. Name one insect from Order Lepidoptera. _____e.g., moth, butterfly_____

130

Lesson 4 Quiz: *What Is Metamorphosis?*

Name: _____   Date: _____

I. Label the kinds of metamorphosis and their stages using the words from the word bank.

Incomplete	*Complete*	*Egg (2)*	*Adult (2)*
Nymph	*Pupa*	*Larva*	

___incomplete___ metamorphosis

Egg   Nymphs   Adult

___complete___ metamorphosis

Egg   Adult

Larva

Pupa

II. Short Answer

1. What do we call the way insects grow? ____metamorphosis____

2. What are the two kinds of metamorphosis? ____incomplete and complete____

3. What are the stages of incomplete metamorphosis? ____egg, nymph, adult____

4. What are the stages of complete metamorphosis? ____egg, larva, pupa, adult____

131

Unit I Test

Name: _____   Date: _____

I. Label the boxes with the missing names (14 total).

Complete Metamorphosis

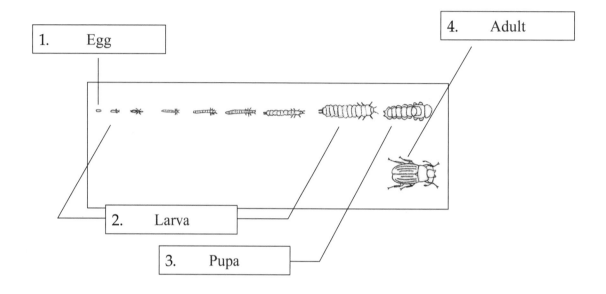

1.   Egg

4.   Adult

2.   Larva

3.   Pupa

5. Odonata	Orthoptera & Dictyoptera	6. Hemiptera	Diptera	7. Coleoptera	Lepidoptera	Hymenoptera

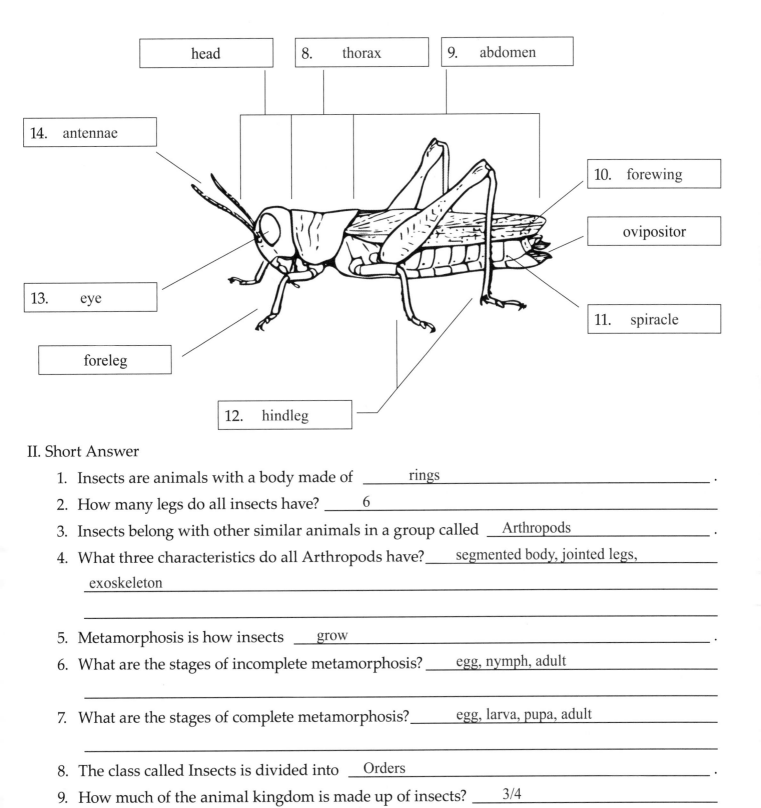

| head | 8. thorax | 9. abdomen |

14. antennae

10. forewing

ovipositor

13. eye

11. spiracle

foreleg

12. hindleg

II. Short Answer

1. Insects are animals with a body made of _____rings_____ .

2. How many legs do all insects have? ____6____

3. Insects belong with other similar animals in a group called ___Arthropods___ .

4. What three characteristics do all Arthropods have?____segmented body, jointed legs,____
   ___exoskeleton___

5. Metamorphosis is how insects ____grow____ .

6. What are the stages of incomplete metamorphosis? ____egg, nymph, adult____

7. What are the stages of complete metamorphosis?_____egg, larva, pupa, adult_____

8. The class called Insects is divided into ___Orders___ .

9. How much of the animal kingdom is made up of insects? ____3/4____

10. Arthropods are divided into Classes based on their ___legs___ .

11. How many legs do Arachnids have?____8____

Lessons 6-7 Quiz: Odonata

Name: _____   Date: _____

I. Identify the main insects of this Order by writing the name of each insect under its picture.

_____   _____
        Dragonfly   Damselfly

II. Fill in the meaning for the Order name.

Order	English meaning
Odonata	toothed

III. Short Answer

1. Insects in this order have _____incomplete_____ metamorphosis.

2. What are the two main characteristics you learned for this order?
   a. ___aquatic nymphs_____
   b. ___needle-like abdomen_____

3. Why are dragonflies not easy to catch? ____They are swift and shy.____

   _____

4. Where may dragonflies be found? ____near calm water, e.g., lakes, ponds____

Lessons 8-9 Quiz: Orthoptera and Dictyoptera

Name: _____   Date: _____

I. Identify the main insects of these orders by writing the name of each insect under its picture.

Grasshopper	Katydid	Cockroach

Mantid	Cricket

II. Fill in the meaning for the Order names.

Order	English meaning	Order	English meaning
Orthoptera	straight-winged	Dictyoptera	net-winged

III. Short Answer

1. Insects in these orders have _____incomplete_____ metamorphosis.

2. What are the two main characteristics you learned for these orders?

   a. _____fan-like hind wings_____

   b. _____leathery front wings_____

3. How do grasshoppers and crickets make their chirping sound? __by rubbing their wings together__

   _____

4. I eat everything I can get, including people's food, and some people say I smell bad. Who am I?
   cockroach
   _____

135

Lessons 10-11 Quiz: Hemiptera

Name: _____   Date: _____

I. Identify the main insects of this Order by writing the name of each insect under its picture.

<u>   Cicada   </u>   <u>   Aphid   </u>   <u>   Leaf-hopper   </u>

<u>   Backswimmer   </u>   <u>   Water Measurer   </u>

II. Fill in the meaning for the Order name.

Order	English meaning
Hemiptera	half-winged

III. Short Answer

1. Insects in this order have _____<u>incomplete</u>_____ metamorphosis.
2. What are the two main characteristics you learned for this order?
   a. <u>first half of wing is rough</u>
   b. <u>tip of wing is smooth</u>
3. What does the water measurer have under his body and on his legs that keeps him from getting wet and sinking? <u>hairs</u>
4. What is called "the singer," "the screamer," and "the squealer"? <u>cicada</u>

Unit II Test

Name: _____   Date: _____

I. Identify the main insects of this unit by writing the name of each insect under its picture. Then circle the order to which it belongs.

Mantid
_____
A. Odonata
(B.) Dictyoptera

Damselfly
_____
A. Hemiptera
(B.) Odonata

Cicada
_____
(A.) Hemiptera
B. Odonata

Cockroach
_____
A. Hemiptera
(B.) Dictyoptera

Cricket
_____
(A.) Orthoptera
B. Odonata

Leaf-hopper
_____
A. Orthoptera
(B.) Hemiptera

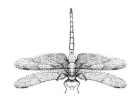

Dragonfly
_____
(A.) Odonata
B. Orthoptera

Water Measurer
_____
(A.) Hemiptera
B. Odonata

Katydid
_____
(A.) Orthoptera
B. Odonata

Aphid
_____
A. Odonata
(B.) Hemiptera

Backswimmer
_____
(A.) Hemiptera
B. Odonata

Grasshopper
_____
(A.) Orthoptera
B. Odonata

II. Fill in the blank with either the meaning for the Order name or the Order.

Order	English meaning
Odonata	toothed
Hemiptera	half-winged
Orthoptera	straight-winged
Dictyoptera	net-winged

III. Circle the answer that makes the statement true.

1. **(Odonata /(Orthoptera)/ Hemiptera)** has fan-like hind wings.

2. **((Odonata /)Orthoptera / Hemiptera)** has aquatic nymphs.

3. **(Odonata / Orthoptera /(Hemiptera))** has smooth wing tips.

4. **(Odonata / Orthoptera /(Hemiptera))** has rough first half of wing.

5. **((Odonata /)Orthoptera / Hemiptera)** has needle-like abdomens.

6. **(Odonata /(Orthoptera)/ Hemiptera)** has leathery front wings.

7. Odonata has **(complete /(incomplete))** metamorphosis.

8. Hemiptera has **(complete /(incomplete))** metamorphosis.

9. Dictyoptera has **(complete /(incomplete))** metamorphosis.

Lessons 13-14 Quiz: Diptera

Name: _____   Date: _____

I. Identify the main insects of this Order by writing the name of each insect under its picture.

House Fly   Horse Fly   Bluebottle

Mosquito   Crane Fly

II. Fill in the meaning for the Order name.

Order	English meaning
Diptera	two-winged

III. Short Answer

1. Insects in this order have _____ complete _____ metamorphosis.
2. What are the two main characteristics you learned for this order?
   a. soft body _____
   b. sucking mouthparts _____
3. What is the name of a fly larva? _____ maggot _____
4. What do the hairs and pad on a fly's foot act like? _____ a sucker _____

_____

Lessons 15-17 Quiz: Coleoptera

Name: _____   Date: _____

I. Identify the main insects of this order by writing the name of each insect under its picture.

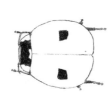

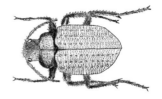

Ladybug/Ladybird   Japanese Beetle   Ground Beetle

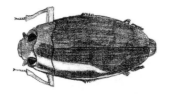

Whirligig Beetle   Sweet Potato Weevil

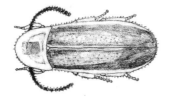
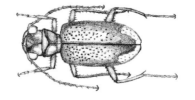

Firefly/Lightning Bug   Tiger Beetle

II. Fill in the meaning for the Order name.

Order	English meaning
Coleoptera	sheath-winged

III. Short Answer

1. Insects in this order have _____ complete _____ metamorphosis.

2. What are the two main characteristics you learned for this order?

   a. ___ front wings are hard _____

   b. ___ front wings meet down the middle of the back ___

3. Why is a ladybug a useful beetle? ___ It eats aphids. ___

4. What are the hard cases over the beetle's back? ___ front wings/elytra ___

140

Unit III Test

Name: _____   Date: _____

I. Identify the main insects of this unit by writing the name of each insect under its picture. Then circle the order to which it belongs.

Mosquito
_____
(A.) Diptera
B. Coleoptera

Sweet Potato Weevil
_____
A. Diptera
(B.) Coleoptera

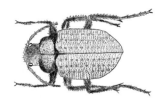

Ground Beetle
_____
A. Diptera
(B.) Coleoptera

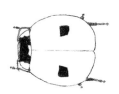

Ladybug
_____
A. Diptera
(B.) Coleoptera

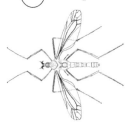

Crane Fly
_____
(A.) Diptera
B. Coleoptera

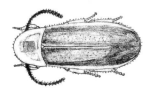

Firefly
_____
A. Diptera
(B.) Coleoptera

Horse Fly
_____
(A.) Diptera
B. Coleoptera

Japanese Beetle
_____
A. Diptera
(B.) Coleoptera

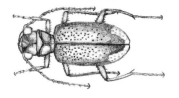

Tiger Beetle
_____
A. Diptera
(B.) Coleoptera

Bluebottle
_____
(A.) Diptera
B. Coleoptera

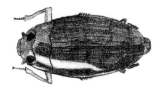

Whirligig Beetle
_____
A. Diptera
(B.) Coleoptera

House Fly
_____
(A.) Diptera
B. Coleoptera

II. Fill in the meaning for the Order name.

Order	English meaning
Coleoptera	sheath-winged
Diptera	two-winged

III. Circle the answer that makes the statement true.
1. (**Diptera** / **Coleoptera**) has soft bodies.
2. (**Diptera** / **Coleoptera**) has hard front wings.
3. (**Diptera** / **Coleoptera**) has front wings that meet down the middle of the back.
4. (**Diptera** / **Coleoptera**) has sucking mouthparts.
5. Diptera has (**complete** / **incomplete**) metamorphosis.
6. Coleoptera has (**complete** / **incomplete**) metamorphosis.

IV. Circle the best answer.
1. What is the name of a fly larva? (**maggot**, worm, grub)
2. Mrs. Fly lays her eggs in: (water, hair, **dead things**)
3. The hard cases over the beetle's back are: (eggs, **wings**)
4. This beetle is fast and fierce: (**tiger beetle**, lady bug, firefly)
5. This water beetle spins round and round: (ground beetle, **whirligig beetle**, Japanese beetle)

Lessons 19-20 Quiz: Moths

Name: _____   Date: _____

I. Identify the main insects of this order by writing the name of each insect under its picture.

_____ Sphinx Moth _____

_____ Luna Moth _____

II. Fill in the meaning for the Order name.

Order	English meaning
Lepidoptera	scale-winged

III. Short Answer

1. Insects in this order have _____ complete _____ metamorphosis.

2. What are the two main characteristics you learned for this order?
   a. _large wings_____
   b. _coiling mouthparts_____

3. What is the difference between a moth's feelers and a butterfly's? __A moth's feelers are__
   feathery and pointed at the end, but a butterfly's feelers are thin and round at the end.
   _____

4. How does a moth hold its wings when it is not flying, or at rest? __It lays its wings back like__
   a roof on a house.
   _____

Lessons 21-22 Quiz: Butterflies

Name: _____   Date: _____

I. Identify the main insects of this Order by writing the name of each insect under its picture.

_____ Monarch Butterfly _____

_____ Swallowtail Butterfly _____

_____ Brush-footed Butterfly _____

_____ Cabbage Butterfly _____

II. Fill in the meaning for the Order name.

Order	English meaning
Lepidoptera	scale-winged

III. Short Answer

1. Insects in this order have _____complete_____ metamorphosis.

2. What are the two main characteristics you learned for this order?

   a. ___large wings_____

   b. ___coiling mouthparts_____

3. When a caterpillar hatches, what does it eat? _It eats the plant on which it was laid._

   _____

4. Does a butterfly fly in a line or in a zig-zag? _It flies in a zig-zag._

Unit IV Test

Name: _____   Date: _____

I. Identify the main insects of this Order by writing the name of each insect under its picture.

Monarch Butterfly

Sphinx Moth

Cabbage Butterfly

Brush-footed Butterfly

Luna Moth

Swallowtail Butterfly

II. Fill in the meaning for the Order name.

Order	English meaning
Lepidoptera	scale-winged

III. Circle the answer that makes the statement true.

1. Lepidoptera has **(complete / incomplete)** metamorphosis.
2. Order Lepidoptera includes the **(cauliflower / cabbage)** butterfly, sphinx moth, monarch butterfly, swallowtail butterfly, and brush-footed butterfly.
3. Other insects in this order include the tiger moth, **(cecropia / capillary)** moth, and skipper butterfly.

145

IV. Circle the best answer.

1. What does a moth spin around itself? (string, ~~silk,~~ cloth)

2. A moth's antennae, or feelers, are: (round, ~~feathery,~~ thin)

3. A butterfly's antennae are: (feathery, pointed, ~~round~~)

4. On its body, a butterfly has a coat of: (feathers, silk, ~~hairs~~)

5. A monarch butterfly is colored: (black, orange, ~~both~~)

V. Short Answer

1. Insects in this order have _____complete_____ metamorphosis.

2. What are the two main characteristics you learned for this order?

   a. large wings

   b. coiling mouthparts

Lessons 24-26 Quiz: Wasps and Ants

Name: _____   Date: _____

I. Identify the wasps and ants by writing the name of each insect under its picture.

| Fire Ant | Carpenter Ant |

| Paper Wasp | Yellow Jacket |

II. Fill in the meaning for the Order name.

Order	English meaning
Hymenoptera	membrane-winged

III. Short Answer

1. Insects in this order have ___complete_____ metamorphosis.

2. What are the two main characteristics you learned for this order?

   a. ___slender waist_____

   b. ___stingers_____

3. How many knobs does a red ant, or fire ant, have? ___2_____

4. Why is the sting of some hook-wing insects like a sword? ___The sting is used to fight with or to kill things for food._____

5. When comparing the shapes of different kinds of wasps, what should you particularly notice?
   Notice the difference in the thread joining the thorax and abdomen.

Lessons 27-29 Quiz: Bees

Name: _____   Date: _____

I. Identify the bees by writing the name of each insect under its picture.

| Worker Honeybee | Drone Honeybee |

| Queen Honeybee | Bumblebee |

II. Fill in the meaning for the Order name.

Order	English meaning
Hymenoptera	membrane-winged

III. Short Answer

1. Insects in this order have _____complete_____ metamorphosis.

2. What are the two main characteristics you learned for this order?

    a. ____slender waist_____

    b. ____stingers_____

3. How many queens rule over a bee hive? _____1_____

4. Which bee wanders aimlessly about the hive and waits for the others to feed them and house them? _____drone honeybee_____

5. What is the little hairy groove on a honeybee's leg called? ____basket____

    _____

6. What happens to the old queen once a new "princess" bee is ready to take over? _____
    The old queen swarms with some of the bees and goes to build a new hive.

Unit V Test

Name: _____   Date: _____

I. Identify the main insects of this Order by writing the name of each insect under its picture.

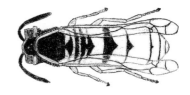

| Fire Ant | Carpenter Ant | Yellow Jacket |

| (worker) Honeybee | Hornet | Paper Wasp |

II. Fill in the meaning for the Order name.

Order	English meaning
Hymenoptera	membrane-winged

III. Circle the answer that makes the statement true.

1. Hymenoptera has **(complete** / **incomplete)** metamorphosis.
2. The sting of some hook-wing insects is like a **(needle /** **sword)**
3. The little hairy groove on a honeybee's leg that is used to carry pollen is called the **(file /** **basket)**.
4. **(Pollination** / **Polymorphosis)** is the way pollen is moved from one plant to another.
5. Mosquitoes can carry **(dengue** / **spotted)** fever and yellow fever.
6. The best natural controller of mosquitoes is the **(crane fly /** **dragonfly)**.

149

IV. Short Answer

1. This order includes insects like the paper wasp, yellow _____jacket_____ ,
   hornet, carpenter ____ant____ , fire ant, honeybee, and_____bumblebee_____ .

2. Insects in this order are characterized by a _____slender waist_____
   and _____stinger_____ .

3. Helpful insects ____pollinate____ plants, decompose___dead___ things,
   control ____pests____ , and make goods.

4. Harmful insects ____destroy____ plants, spread ____disease____ , and damage
   ____goods____ .

5. Other insects in this order include the saw fly, ____mud____dauber, ____bulldog____
   ant, and sweat bee.

Final Test

Name: _____   Date: _____

I. Identify the insects of this study guide by writing the name of each insect under its picture. Then circle the order to which it belongs.

Whirligig Beetle

A. Orthoptera
(B.) Coleoptera
C. Hemiptera

Backswimmer

A. Orthoptera
B. Coleoptera
(C.) Hemiptera

Water Measurer

A. Orthoptera
B. Coleoptera
(C.) Hemiptera

Tiger Beetle

A. Orthoptera
(B.) Coleoptera
C. Hemiptera

Sweet Potato Weevil

A. Orthoptera
(B.) Coleoptera
C. Hemiptera

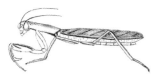

Mantid

(A.) Dictyoptera
B. Coleoptera
C. Hemiptera

Leaf-hopper

A. Orthoptera
B. Coleoptera
(C.) Hemiptera

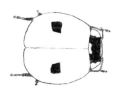

Ladybug

A. Orthoptera
(B.) Coleoptera
C. Hemiptera

Katydid

(A.) Orthoptera
B. Coleoptera
C. Hemiptera

Japanese Beetle

A. Orthoptera
(B.) Coleoptera
C. Hemiptera

Grasshopper

(A.) Orthoptera
B. Coleoptera
C. Hemiptera

Cicada

A. Orthoptera
B. Coleoptera
(C.) Hemiptera

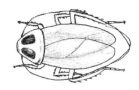

Cockroach	Cricket	Aphid
(A.) Dictyoptera	(A.) Orthoptera	A. Orthoptera
B. Coleoptera	B. Coleoptera	B. Coleoptera
C. Hemiptera	C. Hemiptera	(C.) Hemiptera

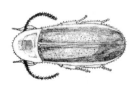

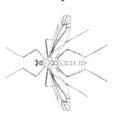

Firefly	House Fly	Bumblebee
A. Orthoptera	A. Orthoptera	A. Odonata
(B.) Coleoptera	B. Coleoptera	B. Lepidoptera
C. Hemiptera	(C.) Diptera	(C.) Hymenoptera
		D. Diptera

Carpenter Ant	Sphinx Moth	Crane Fly
A. Odonata	A. Odonata	A. Odonata
B. Lepidoptera	(B.) Lepidoptera	B. Lepidoptera
(C.) Hymenoptera	C. Hymenoptera	C. Hymenoptera
D. Diptera	D. Diptera	(D.) Diptera

Honeybee	Dragonfly	Luna Moth
A. Odonata	(A.) Odonata	A. Odonata
B. Lepidoptera	B. Lepidoptera	(B.) Lepidoptera
(C.) Hymenoptera	C. Hymenoptera	C. Hymenoptera
D. Diptera	D. Diptera	D. Diptera

Fire Ant
_____

A. Odonata
B. Lepidoptera
C. Hymenoptera
D. Diptera

Bluebottle
_____

A. Odonata
B. Lepidoptera
C. Hymenoptera
D. Diptera

Mosquito
_____

A. Odonata
B. Lepidoptera
C. Hymenoptera
D. Diptera

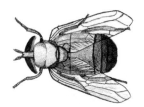

Damselfly
_____

A. Odonata
B. Lepidoptera
C. Hymenoptera
D. Diptera

Swallowtail Butterfly
_____

A. Odonata
B. Lepidoptera
C. Hymenoptera
D. Diptera

Monarch Butterfly
_____

A. Odonata
B. Lepidoptera
C. Hymenoptera
D. Diptera

Horse Fly
_____

A. Odonata
B. Lepidoptera
C. Hymenoptera
D. Diptera

Hornet
_____

A. Odonata
B. Lepidoptera
C. Hymenoptera
D. Diptera

Brush-footed Butterfly
_____

A. Odonata
B. Lepidoptera
C. Hymenoptera
D. Diptera

II. Give the English meaning for the Order names.

Order	English meaning
Coleoptera	sheath-winged
Diptera	two-winged
Hemiptera	half-winged
Hymenoptera	membrane-winged
Lepidoptera	scale-winged
Odonata	toothed
Dictyoptera	net-winged
Orthoptera	straight-winged

III. Tell whether the insects in the orders grow by incomplete or complete metamorphosis. Circle Incomplete or Complete.

1. Coleoptera   Incomplete   (Complete)
2. Diptera   Incomplete   (Complete)
3. Hemiptera   (Incomplete)   Complete
4. Hymenoptera   Incomplete   (Complete)
5. Lepidoptera   Incomplete   (Complete)
6. Odonata   (Incomplete)   Complete
7. Orthoptera   (Incomplete)   Complete
8. Dictyoptera   (Incomplete)   Complete

IV. Give the characteristics for each order.

1. Coleoptera: _____front wings are hard and meet down the middle of the back_____

_____

2. Diptera: _____sucking mouthparts and soft body_____

_____

3. Hemiptera: _____first half of the wing is rough but the tip is smooth_____

_____

4. Hymenoptera: _____slender waist and stinger_____

_____

5. Lepidoptera: _____large wings and coiling mouthparts_____

_____

6. Odonata: _____aquatic nymphs and needle-like abdomen_____

_____

7. Orthoptera and Dictyoptera: _____fan-like hind wings and leathery front wings_____

_____

154